ADVANCED MODULAR MATHEMATICS

Statistics
2

for A and AS level
The University of London modular mathematics syllabus

Gerald Westover
for

NATIONAL
EXTENSION
COLLEGE

CollinsEducational
An Imprint of HarperCollinsPublishers

Published by Collins Educational
An imprint of HarperCollins*Publishers*
77-85 Fulham Palace Road
Hammersmith
London W6 8JB

© National Extension College Trust Ltd 1995
First published 1995
ISBN 0 00 322398 1

This book was written by Gerald Westover for the National Extension College Trust Ltd. Additional material was written by Clifford Taylor. Part of the material was originally written by Graham Smithers and Mik Wisnieski.

Designed by Derek Lee
Cover design and implementation by Derek Lee
Page layout by Mary Bishop
Project editor, Hugh Hillyard-Parker

The author and publishers thank Pat Perkins and Clive Morris for their comments on this book.

Printed and bound in the UK by Scotprint Ltd, Musselburgh

The National Extension College is an educational trust and a registered charity with a distinguished body of trustees. It is an independent, self-financing organisation.

Since it was established in 1963, NEC has pioneered the development of flexible learning for adults. NEC is actively developing innovative materials and systems for distance-learning options from basic skills and general education to degree and professional training.

For further details of NEC resources that support *Advanced Modular Mathematics*, and other NEC courses, contact NEC Customer Services:

National Extension College Trust Ltd
18 Brooklands Avenue
Cambridge CB2 2HN
Telephone 01223 316644, Fax 01223 313586

CONTENTS

Permissions

We are grateful to the following examination boards for permission to reproduce questions from past examination papers in the Exercises at the end of each section.

The Associated Examining Board and University of London Examinations and Assessment Council accept no responsibility whatsoever for the accuracy or method of working in the answers given, which are entirely the responsibility of the author.

Associated Examining Board

Section 1: Exercise 7

Section 2: Exercises 6 & 7

Section 3: Exercise 7

Section 4: Exercises 4 & 10

Section 5: Exercises 2 & 3

Section 6: Exercises 1, 2 & 3

University of London Examinations and Assessment Council

Section 1: Exercises 1, 2, 4, 5 & 6

Section 2: Exercises 3 & 5

Section 3: Exercises 2, 3, 4, 5, 6 & 8

Section 4: Exercises 1, 2, 3, 8 & 9

Section 5: Exercises 5, 6 & 7

Section 6: Exercises 4, 5, 6 & 7

The tables given in Appendices 1–4 are also reproduced with the kind permission of the University of London Examinations and Assessment Council.

T2

Advanced Modular Mathematics

FOREWORD

This book is one of a series covering the University of London Examination and Assessment Council's modular 'A' level Mathematics syllabus. It covers all the subject material for Statistics 2 (Module T2). It also includes advice and guidance on tackling a Statistics project, which is an important part of ULEAC Module T2.

While this series of text books has been structured to match the University of London (ULEAC) syllabuses, we hope that the informal style of the text and approach to important concepts will encourage other readers, whose final examinations are from other examination Boards, to use the books for extra reading and practice.

This book is meant to be *used*: read the text, study the worked examples and work through the exercises, which will give you practice in the basic skills you need for maths at this level. There are many books for advanced mathematics, which include many more exercises: use this book to direct your studies, making use of as many other resources as you can. This book will act as a bridge between your new syllabus and the many older books that can still give even more practice in advanced mathematics.

Exercises are given at the end of each section; these range from the basic to exam-type questions. Many exercises, and worked examples, are based on *applications* of the mathematics in this book. We have given answers to all problems, so that you can check your work.

The National Extension College has more experience of flexible-learning materials than any other body (see p. ii). This series is a distillation of that experience: *Advanced Modular Mathematics* helps to put you in control of your own learning.

1

Sampling and sampling distributions

The major function of statistical methods is to gain knowledge about a population from a sample. There is a wide variety of sampling methods available, but in this first section we will consider three of these:

- random sampling (including use of random numbers)
- stratified sampling
- systematic sampling.

We will then move on to look at the important idea of a sampling distribution which leads into the methods of statistical inference in subsequent sections.

By the end of this section you should understand:

- random sampling (including use of random numbers), stratified sampling and systematic sampling
- unbiased estimators of population parameters
- distribution of the sample mean
- the Central Limit Theorem
- distribution of the sample proportion.

Random sampling

This is by far the most important method of taking samples and simply requires that each member of the population has an equal chance of appearing in the sample. This type of sample can most easily be obtained if there exists a list of all members of the population (**a sampling frame**) and items from the list can be selected in a random unsystematic way (or **without bias**, in statistician's language).

Very often in the sampling process a decision has to be made about whether to allow an item to be chosen repeatedly. If we replace an item after sampling so it has a chance of being selected again, we refer to this as simple random sampling **with replacement**. Sampling **without replacement** happens when an item is not replaced, i.e. once it has been selected, it has no further chance of being selected. Which method we choose depends on the nature of the problem under investigation. For large populations, the distinction between the two methods is minimal, but if the population is small, then sampling without replacement could affect the random nature of the sample.

As a simple illustration of how a random sample might be obtained, consider the problem of obtaining a sample of ten dates from the days of a year (not a leap year). The dates from 1st January to 31st December could be written on to cards, placed in a container, shuffled and then 10 cards could be selected from the container. No particular date is more likely to turn up than any other and each has a chance of $\frac{1}{365}$ of being selected.

A useful technique for larger populations is to use tables of random numbers (see Appendix 1 at the end of the book). These tables consist of blocks of digits, 0 to 9, which have been generated in such a way that there is no bias towards any of the ten digits. The blocks have no particular significance – they are simply there to help with reading the tables. Most random number tables are generated by a computer program and some calculators can generate three-digit random numbers by a similar means.

The normal format for a random number generated by a calculator is as a three-digit decimal. By ignoring the decimal point (to which no significance should be attached), these numbers can just be used as random sequences consisting of three digits. To generate a random number consisting of five digits for example, it would be perfectly valid to generate two random numbers via the calculator and ignore the third digit of the second number.

Returning to the problem of selecting 10 dates from the year, how might random numbers help here?

We need to ensure that each date has an equal chance of occurring. It would therefore be *incorrect* to number the days as follows:

1	1st January
2	2nd January
.	
.	
.	
364	30th December
365	31st December

the reason being that whereas the digit 1 has a probability of $\frac{1}{10}$ of appearing, the sequence of digits 365 has a probability of $\frac{1}{1000}$ $(= \frac{1}{10} \times \frac{1}{10} \times \frac{1}{10})$ of appearing so we would produce a sample very biased towards dates early in the year. So we must ensure as a first step that each random number we associate with a given date has the same chance of appearing. The obvious way in this example is to attach a three-digit number to each date (if the tables are truly random then each three-digit sequence is as likely as any other).

A suitable numbering system would therefore be:

001	1st January
002	2nd January
.	
.	
.	
364	30th December
365	31st December

We now proceed systematically through the random number table and see what turns up. If the sequence 000 or any sequence greater than 365 turns up, we simply reject it and move to the next three-digit sequence. Starting (randomly) at the 3rd line of the tables (we can start anywhere we like), gives the following sequence:

784, 806, 378, 226, 010, 664, 659, etc.

You will notice that we are going to reject a lot of number triples. In fact only 2 out of the first 7 are acceptable for our scheme – 226 and 010.

We can increase the economy of this method in several ways and one way is as follows:

1st January	001	401
2nd January	002	402
	.	.
	.	.
	.	.
30th December	364	764
31st December	365	765

This simple step halves the number of rejected triples and does not affect the random nature of the sample obtained.

Out of the seven triples above we can now make use of 4, giving

784	–	reject
806	–	reject
378	–	reject
226	–	14th August
010	–	10th January
664	–	21st September
659	–	16th September

and we can continue in this way until we have a sample of the required size.

It is quite likely in an example of this type that we would want a sample of 10 different dates, so we would be finding a simple random sample without replacement. In effect, this would mean that if a date happened to come up a second time, we would simply reject it and move to the next random number triple.

Stratified sampling

It may happen that a population under examination falls naturally into sub-groups or *strata*. As a simple example, the population of students in a college is made up of male and female students or full-time and part-time students. Consider a college with 500 registered students who group according to the table:

	Full-time	Part-time
Male	150	100
Female	120	130

If we take a random sample of 50 from the group then we could by chance pick out only full-time students or only male students (each of the $^{300}C_{50}$ possible selections is equally likely under random sampling). We may conduct the sampling when there are proportionately fewer part-time students on campus – quite likely as, by definition, part-time students are at the college less of the time. This would introduce a bias which may be undesirable. **Stratified sampling** provides a means of ensuring that the sampling is in strict proportion to the numbers in each of the 'strata'.

In this case we would divide up our sample of 50 in the ratio
$50 : 100 : 120 : 130$

giving   15 full-time males
         10 part-time males
         12 full-time females
         13 part-time females

and the sample would more properly reflect the natural sub-divisions occurring within the population.

We could use simple random sampling to select the required numbers of students in the sub-categories.

The major advantage of stratified sampling is that the final result – the sample – should reflect any natural sub-division within the population. There are problems associated with this method of sampling, however:

● Firstly, there has to be sufficient information about the population to enable the person taking the sample to delineate the sub-divisions. Such information may not be readily accessible or it may be confidential.

● It is most important that the sub-divisions do not overlap and that they include the whole population. This may involve considerable organisational work, particularly for large populations.

Systematic sampling

In this type of sampling, the candidates for the sample are chosen according to some regular pattern, such as:

● pick out every 10th member from a list of a population

● call at every house numbered 13 or 27 from the houses on an estate

● select every 300th item from a factory production line for quality control testing.

One advantage of such a method is that it is a fairly simple procedure to carry out – for example, a computer program could probably control the third example given above. This method also has the obvious advantage of being simple to explain to somebody who might be employed in taking a sample and therefore may reduce the costs of taking a sample.

A major disadvantage is that the samples obtained are no longer truly random and therefore the data obtained from them must be used with care. If may be, for example, in the factory production line that every 300th item produced is faulty as a result of some fault in the machinery which produces a fault in a regular way, e.g. if every nth item is faulty and n is a factor of 300, then this would not be picked up by the sampling procedure.

You should now be able to answer Exercises 1–2 on page 13.

Sampling distributions of statistics

If we take a sample from a population with (unknown) mean μ, then a natural choice for an *estimate* of the value of μ, the population mean, is the calculated value of $\bar{x}$. $\bar{x}$ is called a **point estimate** for μ.

If we were to take many samples of a given size from the population, we would be surprised if each sample gave the same value for $\bar{x}$. Indeed if we were to do this, we could obtain a whole range of values for $\bar{x}$, draw up a frequency table of the values and calculate an average value of all of the $\bar{x}$'s. We would be treating $\bar{x}$ as if it were itself a value from a new random variable $\bar{X}$.

The random variable $\bar{X}$ is called an **estimator** of the population mean μ, and its specific value $\bar{x}$ calculated from the sample is called an **estimate** of the population mean μ.

5

The distribution of the random variable $\overline{X}$ is called the **sampling distribution of the mean** (or alternatively the **distribution of the sample mean**), and it has some useful and remarkable properties.

Throughout the following we will consider a population having mean μ and variance σ^2 (not necessarily known to us) and a sample of n independent observations (a random sample of size n) where for each observation X_i

$$E(X_i) = \mu$$
$$Var(X_i) = \sigma^2$$

i.e. each observation is a value of a random variable with the same distribution as the population from which it is drawn.

Let $\overline{X} = \dfrac{1}{n}(X_1 + X_2 + \ldots + X_n)$

then the mean of this distribution is

$$
\begin{aligned}
E(\overline{X}) \quad &= \quad E\big[\tfrac{1}{n}(X_1 + X_2 + \ldots + X_n)\big] \\[6pt]
&= \quad \frac{1}{n}E(X_1 + X_2 + \ldots + X_n) \\[6pt]
&= \quad \frac{1}{n}\big(E(X_1) + E(X_2) + \ldots + E(X_n)\big)
\end{aligned}
$$

$$
\begin{aligned}
\text{giving } E(\overline{X}) \quad &= \quad \frac{1}{n}(\mu + \mu + \ldots + \mu) \\[6pt]
&= \quad \frac{1}{n}(n\mu) = \mu
\end{aligned}
$$

In other words the expected or average value of the sample mean is precisely equal to the population mean.

$\overline{X}$ is, as a result of this property, called an **unbiased estimator of** μ and correspondingly $\overline{x}$, the value of $\overline{X}$ which we find for a particular sample, is called an **unbiased estimate** of μ.

We can also think about the variance of the random variable $\overline{X}$.

$$
\begin{aligned}
Var(\overline{X}) \quad &= \quad Var\big[\tfrac{1}{n}(X_1 + X_2 + \ldots + X_n)\big] \\[6pt]
&= \quad \frac{1}{n^2}\big[Var(X_1) + Var(X_2) + \ldots Var(X_n)\big] \\[6pt]
&= \quad \frac{1}{n^2}(\sigma^2 + \sigma^2 + \ldots + \sigma^2) \\[6pt]
&= \quad \frac{n\sigma^2}{n^2} = \frac{\sigma^2}{n}
\end{aligned}
$$

i.e. the variance of $\overline{X}$ is equal to the variance of the population divided by the sample size.

The square root of this, the standard deviation of $\overline{X}$, is called the **standard error** of the mean.

So far we have:

$\overline{X}$ is the sample mean

$E(\overline{X}) = \mu$, the population mean

$Var(\overline{X}) = \dfrac{\sigma^2}{n}$, the population variance divided by the sample size

Standard error of $\overline{X} = \sqrt{Var(\overline{X})} = \dfrac{\sigma}{\sqrt{n}}$

The standard error is used extensively in Section 2.

There is one more question to be answered concerning the sampling distribution of the mean. The answer is now provided.

The Central Limit theorem

In Module T1 we met the important fact that a sum of independent normal random variables is itself a normal variable.

i.e.   if $X_1 \sim N(\mu_1, \sigma_1{}^2)$, $X_2 \sim N(\mu_2, \sigma_2{}^2) \ldots X_n \sim N(\mu_n, \sigma_n{}^2)$

then $X_1 + X_2 + \ldots + X_n \sim N(\mu_1 + \mu_2 + \ldots + \mu_n, \sigma_1{}^2 + \sigma_2{}^2 + \ldots + \sigma_n{}^2)$

$$\sim N\left(\sum_{i=1}^{n} \mu_i, \sum_{i=1}^{n} \sigma_i^2 \right)$$

Now if our parent population is a normal distribution and we think of our random sample as a series of independent normal random variables with $E(\overline{X}) = \mu$ and $Var(\overline{X}) = \dfrac{\sigma^2}{n}$

then the distribution of $\overline{X}$ will itself be a normal distribution according to the result above (each observation being of a normal variable).

Hence if the sample is drawn from a population with a normal distribution we have

$$\overline{X} \sim N\left(\mu, \frac{\sigma^2}{n} \right)$$

and this result is true for any sample size n.

A more powerful result (the derivation of which is not required for 'A' level) states that if $Y = X_1 + X_2 + X_3 + \ldots + X_n$ and n is 'sufficiently large' then Y is approximately normal regardless of the distributions of the individual X_i's. This is a very powerful result known as the **Central Limit theorem** and for our purposes it enables us to conclude that:

$$\bar{X} \sim N\left(\mu, \frac{\sigma^2}{n}\right)$$

where this result is true for all $n \geq 1$ if samples are drawn from a normal population
and is approximately true for 'sufficiently large' n if the samples are drawn from a population which is not normal.

The phrase 'sufficiently large' is not an easy one to put actual values to as it will depend on the nature of the distribution. For a binomial distribution with $p = \frac{1}{2}$ the value of n could be fairly small for the approximation to be good since with $p = \frac{1}{2}$ the binomial distribution has the same symmetry as the normal distribution.

As p gets further away from $\frac{1}{2}$ so n would have to be correspondingly larger for a good approximation. In general the more skewed a distribution, the larger n would have to be for an approximation to be a good one. It may be assumed in examination questions that the values of the sample size given are sufficiently large for the result to apply.

Example

If $X \sim N(15, 25)$ and a sample of size 10 is drawn from this distribution, find the probability that sample mean is between 14 and 16.5.

Solution

Since the question is asking about the sample mean we need to consider the distribution

$$\bar{X} \sim N\left(15, \frac{25}{10}\right)$$

and for this distribution we find

$$P(14 < \bar{X} < 16.5)$$

By the usual standardisation procedure we have

$$P(14 < \bar{X} < 16.5) = P\left(\frac{14 - 15}{\sqrt{\frac{25}{10}}} < Z < \frac{16.5 - 15}{\sqrt{\frac{25}{10}}}\right)$$

$$= P(-0.6325 < Z < 0.9487)$$

$$= 0.565 \ (3 \text{ d.p.})$$

Example	If $X \sim B(300, 0.7)$ and a sample of size 50 is taken from this distribution, find the probability that the sample mean is between 205 and 213.
Solution	$n = 50$ is sufficiently large for the Central Limit theorem to apply.

The mean of $X = 300 \times 0.7 = 210$

variance of $X = 300 \times 0.7 \times 0.3 = 63$

and so $\overline{X} \sim N\left(210, \dfrac{63}{50}\right)$

$$P(205 < \overline{X} < 213) = P\left(\frac{200-205}{\sqrt{\dfrac{63}{50}}} < Z < \frac{213-210}{\sqrt{\dfrac{63}{50}}}\right)$$

$$= P(-4.4544 < Z < 2.6726)$$

$$= 0.9962$$

You should now be able to complete Exercises 3–4 on pages 13–14.

An unbiased estimator of population variance

We noted earlier that $E(\overline{X}) = \mu$ and we referred to this property by saying that $\overline{X}$ is an unbiased estimator of μ.

Now it turns out that the quantity $\dfrac{\Sigma(x_i - \overline{x})^2}{n}$ does *not* have the property that its expectation equals σ^2.

On average it under-estimates the value of σ^2 and is therefore a biased estimator of σ^2. A minor adjustment provides us with an estimator s^2 which does have the desired property of being unbiased, i.e. of giving good results *on average*.

$$s^2 = \left(\frac{n}{n-1}\right) \frac{\Sigma(x_i - \overline{x})^2}{n}$$

is an unbiased estimator for σ^2, where n is the size of the sample.

So, to provide us with an unbiased estimator of σ^2, first find $\dfrac{\Sigma(x_i - \bar{x})^2}{n}$ or

equivalently and more simply $\dfrac{\Sigma x_i^2}{n} - \bar{x}^2$, and then multiply by the

factor $\dfrac{n}{n-1}$.

It should be noted that if n is large then multiplying by this factor will not make much difference,

e.g. if $n = 500$ then we would work out $\dfrac{500}{499} \times \dfrac{\Sigma(x_i - \bar{x})^2}{500}$.

However in examinations it is correct to use this factor anyway.

The distribution of a sample proportion

If we consider an attribute of a population (e.g. left-handedness), then there will be a proportion of the population p which is left-handed. If we take a sample of size n from the population then the number in the sample which have the property of being left-handed is a random variable X which is binomial with parameters n and p, i.e. $X \sim B(n, p)$.

The quantity $\hat{p} = \dfrac{x}{n}$, where x is the actual number in the sample which have the attribute (left-handedness), is an unbiased estimator of p

since $E(\hat{p})\ =\ E\left(\dfrac{X}{n}\right)\ =\ \dfrac{1}{n} E(X)\ =\ \dfrac{1}{n} np = p$

and $\text{Var}(\hat{p}) = \text{Var}\left(\dfrac{X}{n}\right)\ =\ \dfrac{1}{n^2} \text{Var}(X)\ =\ \dfrac{1}{n^2} np(1-p)$

$$= \dfrac{p(1-p)}{n}$$

The distribution of a sample proportion therefore has

$$\text{Mean} = p, \ \text{variance} = \dfrac{p(1-p)}{n}$$

and it also happens to be a binomial distribution (since division by n will not change the nature of the distribution).

As usual with a binomial distribution, if n is sufficiently large we can approximate this by a normal distribution and conclude that

$$P_s \sim N\left(p, \dfrac{p(1-p)}{n}\right)$$

[Note: you may also meet a variation of this notation, where the sample statistic is denoted as p (instead of $\hat{p}$) and the population statistic is denoted as π (instead of p).]

Combining means and variances of samples

To end this section we will look at a couple of examples which involve combining means and variances of samples.

Example

Suppose that 12 people have an average (mean) weight of 70 kg and a further 8 people have an average weight of 68 kg. What will be the average weight of all 20 people?

Solution

Following the methods used in weighted averages, we proceed as follows:

12   people, mean of 70 kg $\therefore \dfrac{\Sigma x}{12} = 70$ $\therefore \Sigma x = 840$

8   people, mean of 68 kg $\therefore \dfrac{\Sigma y}{8} = 68$ $\therefore \Sigma y = 544$

$\therefore$ 20   people have a mean of $\dfrac{\Sigma x + \Sigma y}{20} = \dfrac{840 + 544}{20} = 69.2 \text{ kg}$

Example

Suppose that 12 people have a mean weight of 70 kg, with a standard deviation of 2 kg, and that a further 8 people have a mean weight of 68 kg, with a standard deviation of $\sqrt{3}$ kg. What will be the mean and standard deviation for all 20 people?

Solution

We've seen already that the combined mean is 69.2 kg but what about the standard deviation?

The formula for the variance can be written as:

$$\text{Variance} = \frac{\Sigma x^2}{n} - \bar{x}^2$$

This can be rearranged to give:

$$\text{Variance} + \bar{x}^2 = \frac{\Sigma x^2}{n} \text{ or } \Sigma x^2 = n\,(\text{Variance} + \bar{x}^2).$$

It's this latter formula that can be used to solve our problem of combining variances.

12 people, $\bar{x} = 70$, $s^2 = 4$ $\therefore \Sigma x^2 = 12\,(4 + 70^2) = 58\,848$

8 people, $\bar{y} = 68$, $s^2 = 3$ $\therefore \Sigma y^2 = 8\,(3 + 68^2) = 37\,016$

$\therefore$ 20 people have a variance of

$$\frac{\Sigma x^2 + \Sigma y^2}{20} - 69.2^2 = \frac{58\,848 + 37\,016}{20} - 69.2^2 = 4.56$$

$\therefore$ 20 people have a standard deviation of 2.14 kg

You should now be able to answer Exercises 5–7 on page 14.

Practical exercises

Statistics is by its very nature a practical subject and some experience of collecting and analysing data is essential for a good understanding of the techniques and problems which can arise. As we proceed through Module T2, we encounter several techniques for analysing data and at the end of each section, some practical exercises will be suggested which use these techniques.

You may be able to use these practical exercises – called 'Project exercises' – as part of your work on a full 'A' level project or they may give you ideas about a project you would be interested in carrying out. Section 7 of this book is devoted to tackling an 'A' level Statistics project and will help you formulate your ideas clearly.

The 'A' level syllabus booklets published by the Examination Boards give some suggestions for projects, and students whose 'A' level subjects include Geography, Economics or Biology (for example) should meet many situations where it is necessary to collect and analyse some data. Certainly any project work will involve the use of sampling from a well defined population. Such data (collected for a specific purpose) is called **primary data**.

It is possible to use data which has been collected by somebody else. Such data is called **secondary data** and useful sources of secondary data can be found in public or other libraries, e.g. *The Annual Abstract of Statistics* and *The Monthly Digest of Statistics*. These publications include data about such things as employment and income levels in the UK. If secondary data is used in a project, then it must be referenced in the work.

The first exercises are concerned with obtaining samples. The data obtained will prove useful in later exercises and it is therefore worth keeping a record of it.

PROJECT EXERCISES

1 The financial pages of some newspapers (e.g. *The Times, The Guardian*) include data about share prices of companies quoted on the Stock Exchange. Use random numbers to obtain a sample of 50 companies from those listed. For each company, record its highest and lowest share values for the year and its current value.

2 How accurately can people estimate the length of a time interval? Choose a random sample of people (fellow students or friends) and ask them to give their estimate of a time interval of, say, 10 seconds.

Record the error, positive or negative, for each subject.

Calculate the mean and variance for the data and present it graphically.

3 Generate a population of 1000 numbers in a given range (say between 50 and 100). Find μ and σ^2.

Select a random sample of size 40 from the population and work out $\bar{x}$ and s^2 for the sample.

Repeat for a further 99 samples from the population, giving 100 values for $\bar{x}$ and 100 values for s^2.

Graph the values for each after grouping suitably and confirm from the graph for $\bar{x}$ that the distribution is approximately $N\left(\mu, \dfrac{\sigma^2}{40}\right)$

Confirm that $E(s^2) = \sigma^2$.

EXERCISES

1 (a) State a situation in which you would consider using

(i) a systematic sample

(ii) a stratified sample

when sampling from a population.

Give a specific example in each case.

(b) Give one advantage and one disadvantage associated with stratified sampling.

2 A college of 3000 students has students registered in four departments, Arts, Science, Education and Crafts. The Principal wishes to take a sample from the student population to gain information about likely student response to a rearrangement of the college timetable so as to hold lectures on Wednesday, previously reserved for sports.

What sampling method would you advise the Principal to use? Give reasons to justify your choice.

3 (a) A sample of size 20 is taken from a population which has a Normal distribution with mean = 50, variance = 16. Find the probability that the sample mean is greater than 52.

(b) A sample of size 50 is taken from a population with mean 38 and variance 20. Find the probability that the sample mean is less than 36.

(You may assume that the sample size is sufficiently large for the Central Limit theorem to apply).

4 The mean height of a sample of 15 boys is 1.38 m and the mean height of a sample of 20 girls is 1.22 m.

Find the mean height of the combined sample of boys and girls.

5 The number of errors, x, on each of 200 pages of typescript was monitored. The results when summarised showed that

$$\Sigma x = 920 \quad \text{and} \quad \Sigma x^2 = 5032$$

(a) Calculate the mean and the standard deviation of the number of errors per page.

A further 50 pages were monitored and it was found that the mean was 4.4 errors and the standard deviation was 2.2 errors.

(b) Find the mean and the standard deviation of the number of errors per page for the 250 pages.

6 The table below summarises the number of breakdowns on a stretch of motorway on 30 randomly selected days.

Number of breakdowns (x)	3	4	5	6	7	8	9	10	11
Numbers of days (f)	3	4	2	5	3	6	3	1	3

(a) Calculate unbiased estimates of the mean and the variance of the number of breakdowns

Thirty more days were randomly sampled and this sample had a mean of 7.5 breakdowns and a standard deviation of 2.6 breakdowns.

(b) Treating the 60 results as a single sample obtain further unbiased estimates of the population mean and the population variance.

(c) State, giving your reason, which of these two sets of estimates you would prefer to use.

7 A small shop has two checkouts which are operated by Dharmesh and Errol. Cash customers may use either checkout. Customers paying by cheque or credit card must use Dharmesh's checkout.

During the last hour before closing on a particular day, Errol served 40 customers who spent a total of £168.

(a) Given that $\Sigma x^2 = 784$ calculate the arithmetic mean and the standard deviation of the amount spent by this population of 40 customers.

In the same hour Dharmesh served 25 customers. The amounts they spent had a mean of £5.50 with a standard deviation of £2.50.

(b) Calculate the mean expenditure for all 65 customers served in the last hour.

The amount spent by each customer can be found by examining the till roll.

(c) Explain to the manager how random sampling numbers could be used to obtain a simple random sample (i.e. without replacement) of size 5 from the amounts spent by the 40 customers served by Errol.

It is thought that the data above are typical of all opening hours of the shop. It is suggested that in order to estimate the mean amount spent by customers on another day a random sample of size 5 from Dharmesh's customers and of size 8 from Errol's customers should be taken.

(d) Suggest a possible reason for choosing these figures.
Give a reason why it might be preferable to increase the proportion of Dharmesh's customers in the sample.

[AEB]

SUMMARY

Now that you have completed this section you should understand:

- random sampling including use of random number tables
- the advantages and disadvantages of stratified and systematic sampling
- Central Limit theorem, i.e. $\bar{X} \sim N\left(\mu, \dfrac{\sigma^2}{n}\right)$
- unbiased estimates of μ and σ^2

$\bar{X}$ is an unbiased estimator of μ

$\left(\dfrac{n}{n-1}\right) \dfrac{\Sigma(x_i - \bar{x})^2}{n}$ is an unbiased estimate of σ^2.

2

Confidence intervals

We have seen in Section 1 that $\bar{x}$ is an unbiased estimate of μ but that $\dfrac{\Sigma(x_i - \bar{x})^2}{n}$ is not an unbiased estimate of σ^2. However if we use $s^2 = \left(\dfrac{n}{n-1}\right)s^2$, then we do have an unbiased estimate of σ^2. We also noted that if n is large then $\dfrac{n}{n-1}$ is effectively equal to one. For general guidance, in examinations it is probably safer to use the factor $\dfrac{n}{n-1}$ regardless of the size of n. $\bar{x}$ and s^2 are called *unbiased point estimates* of μ and σ^2.

Point estimates $\bar{x}$ and s^2 are unlikely to give the true values of the population parameters. The only way in which we can be absolutely sure of the values of μ and σ^2 is to use the whole population as a sample. An alternative to point estimation, which makes use of the Central Limit Theorem, is to provide a range of values within which we can have reasonable confidence that μ lies. (The problem of finding such intervals for σ^2 is not part of the 'A' level syllabus.)

By the end of this section you should be able to:

- calculate a confidence interval for a population mean and a population proportion
- explain what a confidence interval represents

Important properties of normal distributions

If $X \sim N(\mu, \sigma^2)$, then it is possible to show that approximately 95% of the probability distribution lies within the interval $\mu - 2\sigma, \mu + 2\sigma$; in other words, 95% of the distribution is within two standard deviations of the mean. This applies to *any* normal distribution, but we will illustrate first with a specific case.

Example	Let $X \sim N(15, 4^2)$
	Find $P(7 < X < 23)$ $\quad$ (i.e. find $P(15 - 8 < X < 15 + 8)$)

Solution	As usual let $Z = \dfrac{X - 15}{4}$

$$\text{then } P(7 < X < 23) = P\left(\frac{7 - 15}{4} < Z < \frac{23 - 15}{4}\right)$$

$$= P(-2 < Z < 2)$$

$$= 0.954 \text{ (from the tables in Appendix 2)}$$

The more general case proceeds as follows:

Example	Let $\quad X \sim N(\mu, \sigma^2)$
	Find $\quad P(\mu - 2\sigma < X < \mu + 2\sigma)$

Solution	Let $\quad Z = \dfrac{X - \mu}{\sigma}$

Then $\quad P(\mu - 2\sigma < X < \mu + 2\sigma)$

$$= P\left(\frac{\mu - 2\sigma - \mu}{\sigma} < Z < \frac{\mu + 2\sigma - \mu}{\sigma}\right)$$

$$= P(-2 < z < 2)$$

$$= 0.954 \qquad \text{(as before)}$$

This example illustrates the so called '2σ-rule', i.e. the fact that for any normal distribution approximately 95% of the distribution lies within the interval $\mu \pm 2\sigma$.

You should now be able to complete Exercise 1 on page 24.

Confidence intervals for μ

In Section 1 we met a statement of the important Central Limit Theorem, i.e. that the statistic $\overline{X} \sim N\left(\mu, \dfrac{\sigma^2}{n}\right)$ where n is the sample size. We can now use the properties of the normal distribution to calculate intervals which contain μ with a certain probability.

A slight modification to the last example would show that
$P(-1.96 \leq Z \leq 1.96) = 0.95$ more closely, i.e. we need to replace 2 by 1.96 to get closer to the desired value of 0.95 or 95%, and in subsequent work we will use the value 1.96 rather than 2.

Following through the working of that example with $\bar{X}$ gives

$$\bar{X} \sim N\left(\mu, \frac{\sigma^2}{n}\right) \quad \Rightarrow Z = \frac{\bar{X} - \mu}{\frac{\sigma}{\sqrt{n}}} \sim N(0, 1)$$

$$\Rightarrow P\left(-1.96 \leq \frac{\bar{X} - \mu}{\frac{\sigma}{\sqrt{n}}} \leq 1.96\right) = 0.95$$

$$\Rightarrow P\left(-1.96 \frac{\sigma}{\sqrt{n}} \leq \bar{X} - \mu \leq 1.96 \frac{\sigma}{\sqrt{n}}\right) = 0.95$$

$$\Rightarrow P\left(1.96 \frac{\sigma}{\sqrt{n}} \geq \mu - \bar{X} \geq -1.96 \frac{\sigma}{\sqrt{n}}\right) = 0.95$$

(multiplying through by –1 and remembering to reverse the inequality signs)

$$\Rightarrow P\left(1.96 \frac{\sigma}{\sqrt{n}} + \bar{X} \geq \mu \geq \bar{X} - 1.96 \frac{\sigma}{\sqrt{n}}\right) = 0.95$$

$\Rightarrow$ the interval

$$\bar{X} \pm 1.96 \frac{\sigma}{\sqrt{n}} \quad \text{contains } \mu \text{ with probability } 0.95$$

Such an interval is called a **95% confidence interval** for the parameter μ and is calculated from the formula

$$\bar{x} \pm 1.96 \frac{\sigma}{\sqrt{n}}$$

where $\bar{x}$ is the sample value for the mean (i.e. the specific value calculated for the random variable $\bar{X}$)

σ^2 is the population variance (if the population variance is unknown then we would have to use the sample to find s^2 and use s instead of σ in the formula)

n is the sample size

Before, we had a point estimate of μ, namely $\bar{x}$. Now we have an interval estimate of μ.

| **Example** | A sample of size 15 from a normal population with unknown mean μ and known variance 25, gives a value of $\bar{x} = 32$. Give a 95% confidence interval for μ. |

| **Solution** | Quoting the result above (which is valid in exams unless the word 'derive' is used) gives |

$$32 \pm 1.96 \frac{5}{\sqrt{15}}$$

$$= 32 \pm 2.53$$

$$= [29.47, 34.53]$$

i.e. $P(29.47 \le \mu \le 34.53) = 0.95$

It is important to realise what this result means. Suppose we took a different sample, then it is highly likely that a different value of $\bar{x}$ would be obtained and therefore a different confidence interval. Confidence intervals are, therefore, *variable quantities* dependent on which sample we happen to select. However, μ is a fixed quantity for a population.

The information which a confidence interval provides is therefore that there is a 95% probability that the interval contains μ.

| **Example** | A sample of size 2000 is taken from a population with unknown distribution, unknown mean μ and unknown variance σ^2.

Calculation gives $\Sigma x_i = 21\,310$, $\Sigma x_i^2 = 458\,650$.

Find a 95% confidence interval for μ. |

| **Solution** | $n = 2000$ is sufficiently large to assume that |

$$\bar{X} \sim N\left(\mu, \frac{\sigma^2}{n}\right) \text{ applies}$$

In this example the population variance is unknown and therefore we have to use the information from the sample to find an estimate for it.

$$\bar{x} = \frac{21\,310}{2000} = 10.66 \text{ (2 d.p.)}$$

$$\frac{\Sigma x_i^2}{n} - \bar{x}^2 = 115.70 \text{ (2 d.p.)}$$

and therefore $s^2 = \dfrac{2000}{1999} \times 115.70 = 115.75$ (2 d.p.)

The confidence interval is therefore

$$10.66 \pm 1.96 \times \frac{10.76}{\sqrt{2000}}$$

$$= 10.66 \pm 0.47$$

$$= [10.19, 11.13]$$

i.e. $P(10.19 \le \mu \le 11.13) = 0.95$

For certain purposes it may be necessary to have an interval within which we would like to be 99% confident or perhaps 90% confident that it contains μ. Usually 95% intervals are used, but in principle we can find a confidence interval of any width.

Example   For the data in the previous example calculate a 99% confidence interval for μ.

Solution   The interval is going to be of the form

$$\bar{x} \pm z \frac{s}{\sqrt{n}}$$

i.e. the only change is in the multiple of $\dfrac{s}{\sqrt{n}}$, the standard error of $\bar{x}$.

To find z we need to know the solution to $P(-z < Z < z) = 0.99$ and from the normal distribution tables (see Appendix 2), we can easily find $z = 2.5758$. Our interval is therefore:

$$10.66 \pm 2.5758 \times \frac{10.76}{\sqrt{2000}}$$

$$= 10.66 \pm 0.62 \text{ (2 d.p.)}$$

$$= [10.04, 11.28] \text{ (2 d.p.)}$$

i.e. $P(10.04 \le \mu \le 11.28) = 0.99$

Note that the 99% interval is wider than the 95% interval for μ. To increase our level of confidence we need to widen the interval.

You should now be able to complete Exercises 2–3 on page 24.

Determination of sample size

One useful variant on the confidence interval calculation relates to the determination of the sample size.

Example

An electronics firm manufactures a printed circuit board which is to be installed in another component. We wish to estimate m (the mean length of the circuit board) to within limits of 0.05 mm. If we know that the standard deviation of the length is 0.5 mm, determine the minimum sample size required:

(a) if we require a probability of 95%

(b) of 90%

(c) of 99%.

Solution

(a) We have:

$$\bar{x} \pm 1.96 \; \frac{\sigma}{\sqrt{n}}$$

and we require $\bar{x} \pm 0.05$ mm. This implies that:

$$1.96 \, \frac{\sigma}{\sqrt{n}} = 0.05 \text{ mm}$$

Given that $\sigma = 0.5$ mm, we can rearrange the expression to determine n:

$$\frac{1.96(0.5)}{\sqrt{n}} = 0.05$$

$$\left(\frac{1.96(0.5)}{0.05}\right)^2 = n$$

$$n = 384.16$$

which must be rounded to 385 to give the required interval size of within 0.05 mm.

Parts (b) and (c) are now straightforward. We only require the equivalent values to replace 1.96 in the last expression.

For (b) we have 1.6449 and for (c) 2.5758 giving:

$$\left(\frac{1.6449(0.5)}{0.05}\right)^2 = n = 270$$

$$\left(\frac{2.5758(0.5)}{0.05}\right)^2 = n = 664$$

It should also be apparent why the sample size must increase so as to give a smaller confidence interval size.

You should now be able to complete Exercises 4–5 on page 25.

Confidence interval for a population proportion

We can also construct confidence intervals when we are dealing with statistics relating to proportions rather than means. Given that the sample statistic is denoted as $\hat{p}$ and the population statistic as p, we know from Section 1 that the sample statistic is approximately $N\left(p, \dfrac{p(1-p)}{n}\right)$.

The corresponding 95% confidence interval is given by:

$$\hat{p} \pm 1.96 \sqrt{\frac{\hat{p}(1-\hat{p})}{n}}$$

Example

A survey has been undertaken of 250 households and it has been found that 58% of these have a video recorder in regular use.

Estimate a 95% confidence interval and interpret the result.

Solution

Here we have $p = 0.58$ and $n = 250$.

The confidence interval is thus:

$$0.58 \pm 1.96 \sqrt{\frac{0.58\,(0.42)}{250}} = 0.58 \pm 0.061$$

That is, we are 95% confident that between 51.9% and 64.1% of all households in the population have a video recorder in regular use. Apart from the calculation itself, exactly the same principles apply that we developed for a confidence interval around the mean.

To summarise, you need to understand that:

1   the 95% confidence limits for the proportion are $\hat{p} \pm 1.96 \sqrt{\dfrac{\hat{p}(1-\hat{p})}{n}}$

2   the 99% confidence limits for the proportion are $\hat{p} \pm 2.5758 \sqrt{\dfrac{\hat{p}(1-\hat{p})}{n}}$.

You should now be able to complete Exercises 6–7 on pages 25–26.

PROJECT EXERCISES

1 How well do people estimate a length of e.g. 15 cm and a time interval of say 20 seconds? Is there a relationship between the two, i.e. are people who estimate lengths accurately also good at estimating times?

Obtain a random sample of subjects and conduct an experiment of the type above (estimating weights could also be used). Illustrate the errors graphically (using absolute values rather than positive or negative errors). How are the errors distributed? Calculate the mean and standard deviation of the errors and confidence intervals for the mean error time.

2 Choose a journey that you regularly take, e.g. by bus or train and measure the time for the journey. How are these times distributed? Find a confidence interval for the mean time for the journey.

3 Counting Ace = 4, King = 3, Queen = 2, Jack = 1, how are the points for a hand of 13 cards distributed? This could be an exercise in simulation or in using a computer.

EXERCISES

1 (a) For $X \sim N(30, 25)$ find $P(25 < X < 35)$

(b) For $X \sim N(\mu, \sigma^2)$ find $P(\mu - \sigma < X < \mu + \sigma)$

2 For the data in the second example on p. 20, find a 90% confidence interval for μ.

3 A machine is regulated to dispense liquid into cartons in such a way that the amount of liquid dispensed on each occasion is normally distributed with a standard deviation of 20 ml.

Find 99% confidence limits for the mean amount of liquid dispensed if a random sample of 40 cartons has an average content of 266 ml.

4 A sample of ten packets of sugar was chosen at random and the contents of each packet were weighed giving the following results in grams:

998.4, 1002.3, 999.2, 1001.5, 997.6, 999.4, 1002.8, 1001.5, 999.5, 1002.6.

Assuming that the sample comes from a population having a normal distribution find:

(a) A 95% confidence interval for μ

(b) A 99% confidence interval for μ

(c) The number of packets which would need to be sampled to give a 95% confidence interval of width less than 1.2.

5 The random variable X is normally distributed with mean μ and variance σ^2.

(a) Write down the distribution of the sample mean $\bar{X}$ of a random sample of size n.

An efficiency expert wishes to determine the mean time taken to drill a fixed number of holes in a metal sheet.

(b) Determine how large a random sample is needed so that the expert can be 95% certain that the sample mean time will differ from the true mean time by less than 15 seconds. Assume that it is known from previous studies that $\sigma = 40$ seconds.

6 It is known that, when letters are sorted by hand, the probability of a letter being misdirected is 0.04. Determine the probability that in a random sample of 40 letters the number misdirected is

(a) at most 2   (b) exactly 1.

State the conditions under which a binomial distribution may be approximated by a normal distribution, and give a reason why this approximation may be useful in practice.

An investigation of a random sample of 2500 letters, sorted by a machine, revealed that 93 had been misdirected.

Calculate an approximate 95% confidence interval for the true proportion of letters misdirected by this machine.

How would you view the claim that machine sorting of letters is more accurate than hand sorting?

[AEB]

7 Employees of a firm carrying out motorway maintenance are issued with brightly coloured waterproof jackets. These come in five different sizes numbered 1 to 5. The last 40 jackets issued were of the following sizes.

2 3 3 1 3 3 2 4 3 2 5 4 1 2 3 3 2 4 5 3 2 4
4 1 5 3 3 2 3 3 1 3 4 3 3 2 5 1 4 4

(a) (i) Find the proportion in the sample requiring size 3. Assuming the 40 employees can be regarded as a random sample of all employees calculate an approximate 95% confidence interval for the proportion, p, of all employees requiring size 3.

(ii) Give two reasons why the confidence interval calculated in (i) is approximate rather than exact.

(b) Your estimate of p is $\hat{p}$.

(i) What percentage is associated with the approximate confidence interval $\hat{p} \pm 0.1$?

(ii) How large a sample would be needed to obtain an approximate 95% confidence interval of the form $\hat{p} \pm 0.1$?

[AEB]

SUMMARY

Now you have completed this section you should be able to calculate:

● a confidence interval for μ, the population mean
● a confidence interval for p, the population proportion
● confidence intervals for levels other than 95%.

Hypothesis testing

INTRODUCTION

We now extend the important idea of statistical inference to look at hypothesis tests.

By the end of this section you should understand:

- null and alternative hypotheses and the interpretation of a hypothesis test
- critical region and significance level of a test
- one-tailed and two-tailed tests
- how to conduct a test on a sample mean from a normal distribution
- how to extend this by using the Central Limit theorem
- how to determine the probabilities of a Type I and Type II error.

The basic ideas

We will illustrate the procedures involved in conducting a hypothesis test by considering in some detail a fairly simple example. The example is not intended to be realistic but serves only to introduce the ideas in as straightforward a way as possible. More realistic examples will be used subsequently.

Consider the following example.

Example

A factory produces objects whose weights come from a distribution $X \sim N(15, 9)$ (in kg). One day the machine breaks down and adjustments are required. When the machine starts up again a single item is weighed and found to weigh 20 kg. The question to be answered is 'have the repairs increased the mean weight of the objects or can we *reasonably expect* an observation this large from the original distribution?'

In this example and subsequently, we will assume that the variance is not altered by the changes that have taken place. In practice this is usually a fair assumption to make (but you should be aware of this assumption).

| **Solution** | To answer the question posed in a formal way we set up two hypotheses. The **null hypothesis** is one which states that no change has taken place. It is always a conservative hypothesis in the sense that it says that things have stayed the same. In this example |

$$H_0 : \mu = 15$$

is the appropriate null hypothesis.

(Note that the null hypothesis is a statement about a *single* parameter value – we are not concerned here with changes to σ^2 or indeed with the unlikely possibility that the distribution changes from being normal.)

The **alternative hypothesis** is one which predicts that a change has taken place; in this example, because of the key word 'increase' in the wording of the problem, the appropriate statement is

$$H_1 : \mu > 15$$

The object of the hypothesis test is now to determine which of H_0 and H_1 is more valid, given the information that we have. As with all situations in statistics we can never have absolute certainty – only a degree of confidence.

What we have to now decide is at what point would we consider the observed value to be too large to come from a distribution N(15, 9) i.e. we need to decide on a value of x in Figure 3.1.

Figure 3.1

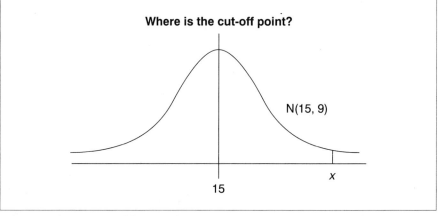

Where is the cut-off point?

N(15, 9)

x

15

This is a decision problem, and a commonly used measure is to have a probability of 0.05 to the right of x.

This is referred to as a **5% significance level.** Now we assume that H_0 is true and follow through the consequences of this assumption.

Under H_0, $X \sim N(15, 9)$

$$\Rightarrow Z = \frac{X - 15}{3} \sim N(0, 1)$$

(this is just the usual standardising process used for any problem involving normal distributions)

Now the problem is transformed into one concerning the standard normal distribution.

Figure 3.2

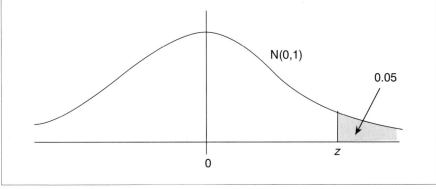

From the normal distribution tables in Appendix 2, we can see that the value of z for which $P(Z > z) = 0.05$ is

$z = 1.6449$

So if our value of $\frac{X - 15}{3}$ which we observe, i.e. $\frac{20 - 15}{3}$, falls to the right of $z = 1.6449$ we will say that the observation of 20 does not fit with H_0.

In fact $\frac{20 - 15}{3} = 1.67$ which is therefore just outside our range for accepting H_0.

The quantity $\frac{X - 15}{3}$ is referred to as the **test statistic** and is essentially compared with the value 1.6449, called the **critical value**, after substituting the observed value of X. The critical value is the boundary of the **critical region** shown in Figure 3.3 and depends on the significance level of the test.

If the value of the test statistic falls in the **acceptance region**, then we accept H_0, i.e. we accept that no change has been observed on the evidence given.

Conversely if it falls in the critical region then we reject H_0 in favour of H_1.

Figure 3.3

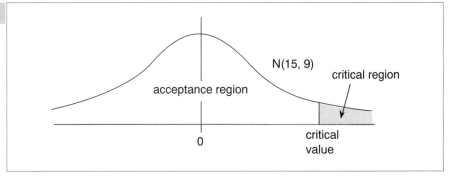

Our conclusion in this particular example is that 'from the data given, there is significant evidence at the 5% level that the population mean has increased.'

In this example a definite increase in μ was tested, but in other circumstances it may be a *decrease* which is more appropriate or even just a change in μ in either direction.

One-tailed and two-tailed tests

Tests of the form

$\qquad H_0 : \mu = k$

$\qquad H_1 : \mu > k$ $\qquad$ (here we are looking for an increase in the parameter)

or $\quad H_0 : \mu = k$

$\qquad H_1 : \mu < k$ $\qquad$ (looking for a decrease)

are referred to as **one-tailed tests** since the critical region lies at just one end of the distribution.

Tests of the form

$\qquad H_0 : \mu = k$

$\qquad H_1 : \mu \neq k$ $\qquad$ (looking for a change)

are referred to as **two-tailed tests** and here the critical region is split into two, e.g. at a 5% level of significance there would be $2\frac{1}{2}\%$ at each end of the distribution. It is important when conducting hypothesis tests that the hypothesis, the nature of the test, and the significance levels, are decided before any data is actually collected.

The next example is a more realistic use of hypothesis testing. The last example relied on testing a single item of data, but in practice a sample of data would be used.

Example	A new type of car has just been launched on the UK market. The manufacturer claims that it averages 46 miles per gallon of petrol. One of the motoring organisations decides to check this claim. They test drive a sample of 150 of the new cars and find that, on average, fuel consumption is 43 mpg, standard deviation 10.2.

Is there any evidence at the 5% significance level to indicate that the test results are different from the manufacturer's claim?

Solution	First we need to establish the hypotheses. The critical words in the problem are 'different from'. We are not asked to test whether they are better or worse, but simply different. This implies a two-tail test and two hypotheses such that:

$$H_0 : \mu = 46$$
$$H_1 : \mu \neq 46$$

This problem is concerned with testing the significance of a mean value calculated from a sample. We are told that our model is $X \sim N(\mu, 10.2^2)$ and wish to test the hypothesis given above, based on the observation that, for a sample of size 150, $\bar{x} = 43$.

Since we are testing a mean value (rather than a single observation as in the previous example), we need to recall from Section 1 that

$$\bar{X} \sim N\left(\mu, \frac{\sigma^2}{n}\right)$$

i.e. in this case

$$\bar{X} \sim N\left(\mu, \frac{10.2^2}{150}\right)$$

Standardising gives

$$Z = \frac{\bar{X} - \mu}{\frac{10.2}{\sqrt{150}}}$$

which when we substitute our values for $\bar{x}$ (the observed value) and μ (the value predicted by the null hypothesis) gives our test statistic.

We get

$$z = \frac{43 - 46}{\frac{10.2}{\sqrt{150}}} = -3.6.$$

The critical values and critical regions are shown in Figure 3.4. These are obtained by splitting the 0.05 into two equal parts, 0.025 at each end, since we are conducting a two–tailed test.

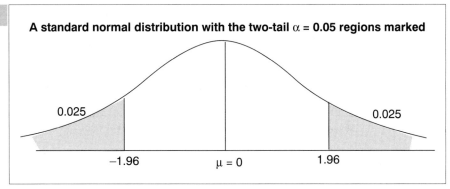

Figure 3.4

A standard normal distribution with the two-tail $\alpha = 0.05$ regions marked

0.025   0.025

−1.96 $\mu = 0$ 1.96

Our test statistic falls into the critical region since $-3.6 < -1.96$ and so therefore we reject H_0 in favour of H_1, i.e. we accept the alternative hypothesis that the test results do not support the manufacturer's claim.

In this example, because of the way in which the problem was stated, i.e. the key phrase 'test results are different from manufacturers claim', it was correct to conduct a two-tailed test. However in practice a decrease in miles per gallon would be more likely to be looked for here (leading to a one-tailed test). However, given the way in which the problem was stated it was correct to conduct a two-tailed test.

You should now be able to answer Exercise 1 on page 42.

Testing the difference between two sample means

It is also possible to apply the same principles to a test involving two samples/populations. Consider the following.

Example   A dietician is testing two different diets on volunteers with a view to assessing weight loss under each diet regime. Under Diet A, 120 people took part and achieved an average weight loss of 450 grams, standard deviation 87 grams. For Diet B, 150 people took part and achieved an average weight loss of 425 grams, standard deviation 95 grams.

Is there any difference, at the 95% significance level, in the effect of these two diets on weight loss?

Solution   Effectively we are posing the question: do the two groups come from different populations, i.e. is there a significant difference between Diet *A* and Diet *B* in terms of weight loss? We shall use the following notation as shown in Table 3.1.

Table 3.1

Diet A	Diet B
$\bar{x}_1 = 450$	$\bar{x}_2 = 425$
$s_1 = 87$	$s_2 = 95$
$n_1 = 120$	$n_2 = 150$
μ_1 unknown	μ_2 unknown

Our hypotheses are then:

$$H_0 : \mu_1 = \mu_2$$
$$H_1 : \mu_1 \neq \mu_2$$
$$\alpha = 0.05 \ \text{(two-tailed test)}$$

Critical values, $z = \pm 1.96$

Under the null hypothesis we are assuming that the distributions

$\bar{X}_1$ (under diet *A*) and $\bar{X}_2$ (under diet *B*) are normal distributions with the same population mean

i.e. $\bar{X}_1 = N\left(\mu, \dfrac{\sigma_1^2}{n_1}\right)$

$\bar{X}_2 = N\left(\mu, \dfrac{\sigma_2^2}{n_2}\right)$

using results from Module T1 we can form the new random variable

$$\bar{X}_1 - \bar{X}_2 \ \sim N\left(\mu - \mu, \ \frac{\sigma_1^2}{n_1} + \frac{\sigma_2^2}{n_2}\right)$$

$$\sim N\left(0, \ \frac{\sigma_1^2}{n_1} + \frac{\sigma_2^2}{n_2}\right)$$

Now if we standardise this we obtain

$$Z = \frac{(\bar{X}_1 - \bar{X}_2) - 0}{\sqrt{\dfrac{\sigma_1^2}{n_1} + \dfrac{\sigma_2^2}{n_2}}}$$

$$= \frac{\bar{X}_1 - \bar{X}_2}{\sqrt{\frac{\sigma_1^2}{n_1} + \frac{\sigma_2^2}{n_2}}}$$

and this is the test-statistic for comparing two means from normal distributions, when the population variances are known.

Now, in this example the population variances under diet A and diet B are presumably unknown. The values of the standard deviations for each sample have, we must assume, been correctly calculated and are unbiased estimates of the respective population standard deviations. Therefore we need to use the given values for the sample standard deviations instead.

Substituting our given values we get

$$z = \frac{450 - 425}{\sqrt{\frac{87^2}{120} + \frac{95^2}{150}}} = 2.2520 \quad (4 \text{ d.p.})$$

The z-value is greater than the critical value for the test (1.96) and so we reject the null hypothesis and conclude that there is a difference between the diets.

You should now be able to complete Exercises 2–3 on page 42.

Hypothesis test for a proportion when the sample is large

Consider the following situation.

Example   A new type of headache relief medicine has been tested on a random sample of the public. Of 250 people taking part in the test, 170 said the new medicine relieved their headache. The company manufacturing this medicine already have a similar product on the market and know that 70% of people using it find it effective.

Is the new product as effective as the old one?

Solution   The sample proportion $\hat{p}$ is an unbiased estimate of the population proportion p. From Section 1 we saw that the sampling distribution of $\hat{p}$ is a binomial random variable P with mean $= p$ and variance $= \frac{p(1-p)}{n}$ where n is the sample size under consideration.

Now if n is of a suitable size we can use the normal approximation to this distribution, where the normal approximation will have the same mean and variance as those for the random variable P.

i.e. $P \approx N\left(p, \dfrac{p(1-p)}{n}\right)$

and standardising gives

$$z = \dfrac{P - p}{\sqrt{\dfrac{p(1-p)}{n}}}$$

giving the test statistic $\dfrac{\hat{p} - p}{\sqrt{\dfrac{p(1-p)}{n}}}$ when our sample proportion is

substituted. The form of this should be remembered.

[You will remember from Section 1 that you may also meet a variation of this notation, where the sample statistic is denoted as p (instead of $\hat{p}$) and the population statistic is denoted as π (instead of p).]

Returning to the example we have:

$n = 250$

$\hat{p} = \dfrac{170}{250}$ (i.e. the proportion of people in the sample whose condition improved.)

$p = 0.70$

$H_0 : p = 0.70$ (i.e. predicting no change from the previous situation)

$H_1 : p < 0.70$ (i.e. is the new proportion significantly less than the old)

1% level of significance (this means the size of the critical region will now be only 1% of the total distribution and this amounts to finding a different critical value – all other aspects of the test remain the same).

one-tailed test

Substituting the given values we have:

$$z = \dfrac{\dfrac{170}{250} - 0.7}{\sqrt{\dfrac{(0.7)\,(0.3)}{250}}}$$

$$= \dfrac{-0.02}{0.029} = -0.69.$$

For our critical value we need the value of z in Figure 3.5.

Figure 3.5

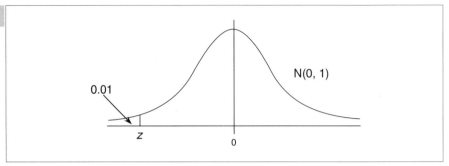

From tables (see Appendix 2), we find $z = -2.3263$.

Since $-0.69 > -2.3263$,

we accept H_0 and conclude that at the 1% significance level the new medicine is at least as effective as the old.

Hypothesis test on the mean of a Poisson distribution

In a similar way to the test for the proportion of a binomial distribution we can test for the mean of a Poisson distribution as the following example illustrates.

Example   A motoring organisation knows that in a particular city area, it will receive an average of 12 calls per hour from its members requiring assistance with a broken-down car. In one particular hour there were 15 call-outs. Does this indicate that the average number of call-outs per hour has increased?

Solution   Recalling from Module 1 that the mean and variance of a Poisson distribution are equal, we have

$$\mu = 12, \sigma^2 = 12 \text{ and } \bar{x} = 15.$$

and $H_0 : \mu = 12$

$H_1 : \mu > 12$

(a one-tailed test since the question asks about a definite increase)

Significance level 1%

Since, if $X \sim P(\mu)$ and μ is sufficiently large, we have $X \approx N(\mu, \mu)$

the test statistic is

$$z = \frac{\bar{x} - \mu}{\sqrt{\mu}} = \frac{14.5 - 12}{\sqrt{12}} = 0.72$$

For the critical value we need to know the value of z shown in Figure 3.6 below.

Figure 3.6

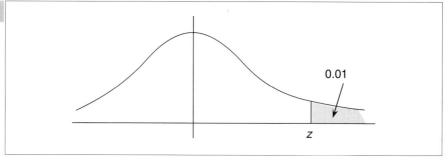

and from tables we find this to be 2.3263.

Our test statistic is well within the acceptance region and so we accept the null hypothesis that no significant increase has occurred.

You should now be able to complete Exercises 4–6 on pages 43–44.

Use of Central Limit theorem in hypothesis testing

We noted earlier that if X is any random variable (discrete or continuous) and our sample size n is sufficiently large, then we can consider a new random variable $\overline{X}$ which will have an approximately normal distribution with parameters μ and $\dfrac{\sigma^2}{n}$ where μ and σ^2 are the mean and variance of X.

i.e. $\overline{X} \approx N\!\left(\mu, \dfrac{\sigma^2}{n}\right)$.

This powerful theorem enables us to conduct hypothesis tests about mean values even if we don't know the nature of the original distribution.

Indeed, it may be that σ^2 is also unknown. In these circumstances it would be necessary to approximate the value of σ^2 by s^2, the unbiased estimator of σ^2.

More generally then, we would have

$$\overline{X} \approx N\!\left(\mu, \dfrac{s^2}{n}\right)$$

We would then use the sample of values to find $\overline{x}$ and s^2 and proceed to test the value of $\overline{x}$ against the value of μ using the test statistic

$$z = \frac{\overline{x} - \mu}{\dfrac{s}{\sqrt{n}}}$$

You should now be able to complete Exercise 7 on page 44.

Type I and Type II errors

Hypothesis tests are not infallible. We may select an unrepresentative sample and therefore reject H_0 when it is true, or accept H_0 when it is false. If we have rejected H_0 when it is true we have made a **Type I error** and the probability that this happens is equal to the significance level α of the test (since we reject H_0 precisely when we fall into the critical region of the test).

This is illustrated for the case of a one-tailed test in Figure 3.7.

Figure 3.7

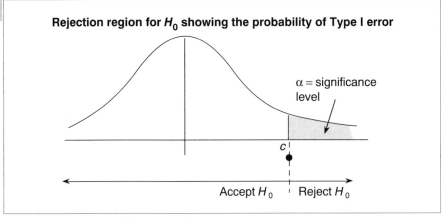

Rejection region for H_0 showing the probability of Type I error

α = significance level

Accept H_0 | Reject H_0

$$P(\text{Type I error}) = P(\text{Reject } H_0 \mid H_0 \text{ is true})$$

$$= \alpha$$

$$= \text{significance level of the test}$$

We have control over Type I errors since we decide the significance level before conducting the test.

However, the more we reduce the probability of a Type I error, the more we increase the probability of a Type II error.

A **Type II error** is made if we accept H_0 when H_0 is in fact false.

i.e. $P(\text{Type II error}) = P(\text{Accept } H_0 \mid H_0 \text{ is false})$

or equivalently $= P(\text{Accept } H_0 \mid H_1 \text{ is true})$.

At the extreme we may decide to always accept H_0 in which case

$\qquad P(\text{Type I error}) = 0$ (the rejection region has been eliminated).

However we would then have

$\qquad P(\text{Type II error}) = 1$

We cannot eliminate errors in hypothesis testing. If we reduce the probability of a Type I error, then we inevitably increase the probability of a Type II error and vice-versa. Which of these should be minimised depends on the nature of the problem.

As an illustration of this dilemma consider the following:

Example   A drug for treating a serious illness has cured patients with a probability of 0.8 for many years. A new drug is discovered and tested on 100 patients and is successful for 84 patients.

Is this a significant improvement?

Solution   The question can only be answered once we have decided on a significance level. If we choose a level of 1% then

$$P(\text{Type I error}) = 0.01$$

(i.e. we will reject H_0 when it is in fact true with probability 0.01)

Taking $H_0 : p = 0.8$

$\qquad\qquad H_1 : p > 0.8$

i.e. conducting a one-tailed test

then if we commit a Type I error we will reject H_0 (and begin to use the new drug) when in fact the old drug performed at least as well. There may be a considerable financial loss as a result.

If we commit a Type II error then we would accept H_0 (i.e. continue to use the old drug) when in fact H_1 is true (i.e. the new drug is better), with the possible consequent loss of life. In this situation it is probably advisable to minimise Type II errors.

$$\text{Test statistic} \quad = \quad \frac{\frac{84}{100} - 0.8}{\sqrt{\frac{(0.8)\,(0.2)}{84}}}$$

$$= \; 0.9165$$

Since $0.9165 < 2.3263$, we accept H_0 and continue to use the old drug.

We now look at a slightly different type of test and a calculation of Type I and Type II probabilities.

| **Example** | A marksman claims he can hit a target 9 times out of ten on average. Find the probability that he hits a target at least 8 times out of 10: |

(a) (i)   if his claim is correct

    (ii)   if in reality he hits or misses the target with equal probability.

(b)   His claim is accepted if, in a trial of 10 shots, he hits the target 8 or more times. Find the probability of Type I and Type II errors for this test.

| **Solution** | (a) (i) $P(\text{Hits target}) = \frac{9}{10}$ |

Number of hits $= X \sim B\left(10, \frac{9}{10}\right)$

$$P(X \geq 8) = P(X = 8) + P(X = 9) + P(X = 10)$$

$$= \,^{10}C_8 \left(\frac{9}{10}\right)^8 \left(\frac{1}{10}\right)^2 + \,^{10}C_9 \left(\frac{9}{10}\right)^9 \left(\frac{1}{10}\right) + \,^{10}C_{10} \left(\frac{9}{10}\right)^{10}$$

$$= 0.930$$

(ii) $P(\text{hits target}) = \frac{5}{10}$

Number of hits $= Y \sim B\left(10, \frac{5}{10}\right)$

$$P(Y \geq 8) = \,^{10}C_8 \left(\frac{1}{2}\right)^8 \left(\frac{1}{2}\right)^2 + \,^{10}C_9 \left(\frac{1}{2}\right)^9 \left(\frac{1}{2}\right) + \,^{10}C_{10} \left(\frac{1}{2}\right)^{10}$$

$$= 0.055$$

(b) H_0 : The man can hit the target 9 times out of 10 on average (what he claims)

H_1 : He can hit the target 5 times out of 10 on average (the reality)

H_0 is accepted if he hits the target at least 8 times out of ten in a test situation.

$P(\text{Reject } H_0 \mid H_0 \text{ is true})$

$$= P(\text{less than 8 hits} \mid p = 0.9)$$
$$= 1 - 0.930 \;\text{(from (a))}$$
$$= 0.07$$
$$= P(\text{Type I error})$$

$P(\text{Accept } H_0 \mid H_1 \text{ is true})$

$$= P(\text{at least 8 hits} \mid p = 0.5)$$
$$= 0.044 \;\text{(from (b))}$$
$$= P(\text{Type II error}).$$

You should now be able to complete Exercises 8–9 on page 45.

Summary of steps involved in hypothesis testing

Hypothesis testing involves some careful decision-making and step-by-step working. The following summary of steps will prove useful in tackling questions based on hypothesis testing.

Step 1: Formulate the null and alternative hypotheses. This will involve establishing a suitable value for μ and determining whether the test is one- or two-tailed.

Step 2: Establish a significance level, α. Sometimes this may be specified in the problem; at other times we may have to make the choice ourselves. The smaller the α value, the more proof we require before rejecting H_0.

Step 3: Obtain the value of z, the critical value, corresponding to the chosen level of significance. It may be useful to sketch the normal distribution at this stage, and the area under the tail(s). This area is the rejection region.

Step 4: Using the appropriate formula calculate the test statistic.

Step 5: Decide whether to reject H_0 by comparing the critical z with the test statistic. If the test statistic is greater than the critical value, reject H_0, otherwise we have no reason to reject the null hypothesis.

PROJECT EXERCISES

1 Compare lengths of sentences in two languages, e.g. English and French. This exercise will require use of random sampling techniques to obtain samples from English and French texts, e.g. novels, working out mean lengths and standard deviations of lengths and then conducting a hypothesis test comparing the means.

2 Are students whose 'A' level choices include mathematics better able to estimate lengths and/or time intervals? Conduct an experiment to test this hypothesis.

3 Can people tell the difference between Coca Cola and a cheaper supermarket brand. Conduct an experiment to test the hypothesis of whether there is any real difference.

EXERCISES

1 An observation $x = 23$ is made. Test at the 5% level whether this observation is likely to have come from the distribution $X \sim N(20, 36)$

2 Explain what you understand by the Central Limit Theorem. An electrical firm claims that the average lifetime of the bulbs it produces is 800 hours with a standard deviation of 42 hours. To test this claim a random sample of 120 bulbs was taken and these bulbs were found to have an average lifetime of 789 hours. Stating clearly your hypotheses and using a 5% level of significance test the claim made by the electrical firm.

3 The random variable X is distributed normally with mean μ and variance σ^2.

Write down the distribution of the sample mean $\overline{X}$ of a random sample of size n.

Records from a dental practice showed that during 1991 the number of minutes per visit spent in the dentist's chair can be taken to be normally distributed with mean 14.5 minutes and standard deviation 2.9 minutes.

(a) Calculate an interval within which 90% of the times spent in the dentist's chair will lie.

In 1992 it was assumed that the standard deviation remained unchanged, and the distribution can be assumed to be normal.

A random sample of 16 consultations gave the following times in minutes.

13.2	18.7	14.9	12.1	11.6	17.2	10.6	9.4
14.6	12.9	11.2	13.5	12.9	11.8	14.1	12.5

(b) For 1992, calculate a 95% confidence interval for the mean length of a visit to the dentist.

It is suggested by the dental practice that the average number of minutes spent in the dentist's chair has decreased between 1991 and 1992.

(c) Stating clearly your hypotheses and using a 5% significance level, investigate this suggestion and draw an appropriate conclusion.

4 An experiment was conducted to compare the drying properties of two paints: Quickdry and Speedicover. In the experiment, 200 similar pieces of metal were painted, 100 randomly allocated to Quickdry and the rest to Speedicover.

The table below summarises the times, in minutes, taken for these pieces of metal to become touch-dry.

	Quickdry	Speedicover
Mean	28.7	30.6
Standard Deviation	7.32	3.51

It is believed that the time taken for paint to become touch-dry is normally distributed.

The manufacturer of Quickdry claims that on average this paint takes 25 minutes to become touch-dry.

(a) Stating clearly your hypotheses and using a 5% significance level, test whether or not these data are consistent with the claim of the manufacturer.

(b) Using a 5% significance level, test whether or not the mean time for Quickdry to become touch-dry is less than that for Speedicover. State your hypotheses clearly.

(c) Suggest two reasons why the time for each paint to become touch-dry is not constant.

5 Over a long period of time it has been found that in Enrico's restaurant the ratio of non-vegetarian to vegetarian meals ordered is 3 to 1.

During one particular day at Enrico's restaurant, a random sample of 20 people contained 2 who ordered a vegetarian meal.

(a) Carry out a significance test to determine whether or not the proportion of vegetarian meals ordered that day is lower than is usual. State clearly your hypotheses and use a 10% significance level.

(b) State an assumption you need to make when carrying out this test. Give one reason why this assumption may well not hold in practice.

6 State conditions under which the Poisson distribution is a suitable model to use in statistical work.

The number of typing errors per 1000 words made by a typist has a Poisson distribution with mean 2.5.

(a) Find, to 3 decimal places, the probability that in an essay of 4000 words there will be at least 12 typing errors.

The typist types 3 essays, each of length 4000 words.

(b) Find the probability that each contains at least 12 typing errors.

A new typist is employed and in a 3000 word essay, 4 typing errors were found.

(c) Perform a significance test at the 5% level to decide whether or not the number of typing errors has decreased. State clearly the hypotheses you use.

[AEB]

7 A food processor produces large batches of jars of jam. In each batch the gross weight of a jar is known to be normally distributed with standard deviation 7.5 g.

The gross weights, in grams, of a random sample from a particular batch were:

517, 481, 504, 482, 503, 497, 512, 487, 497, 503, 509

(a) Calculate a 90% confidence interval for the mean gross weight of this batch.

(b) The manufacturer claims that the mean gross weight of a jar in a batch is at least 502 g. Test this claim at the 5% significance level.

(c) Explain why, if the manufacturer had claimed that the mean gross weight was at least 496 g, no further calculations would be necessary to test this claim.

8 Define Type I and Type II errors.

At a large school, there was an investigation of the distances from the school to the children's homes.

The distance from school, X kilometres, measured to the nearest kilometre, was recorded for each of a random sample of 60 children and the results summarised as follows:

$$\Sigma x = 464, \ \Sigma x^2 = 5769.$$

(a) Calculate unbiased estimates of the mean and the variance of the population from which this sample was drawn.

It is claimed that children from the school live on average less than 10 kilometres away from school.

(b) Stating any assumptions you make, use your results from (a) to test this claim. State clearly your hypotheses and use a 5% level of significance.

9 To test whether a coin is fair, it is tossed 20 times and if a head comes up more than 16 times then it is considered to be biased.

With a null hypothesis $H_0 : p = \frac{1}{2}$ where p is the probability of getting a head, find the probabilities of Type I and Type II errors given that p is in fact $\frac{5}{8}$.

SUMMARY

Now you have completed this section you should be able to:

- formulate a null hypothesis and alternative hypothesis (one-tailed or two-tailed appropriately)
- understand the concept of significance level
- conduct a test to determine whether a sample could have come from a specified population
- conduct a test comparing the means of normal distributions
- conduct tests on sample proportions and on the mean of a Poisson distribution
- be able to calculate Type I and Type II errors.

4

The χ^2 distribution

INTRODUCTION In this section we extend the types of hypothesis test we can undertake by examining the χ^2 (chi-squared – from the Greek letter pronounced 'ki') distribution. Unlike the other probability distributions we have introduced, we are not normally interested in this one for its own sake, but in terms of how it can be used in a number of specific types of situation.

By the end of this section you should be able to:

- appreciate the usefulness of the χ^2 distribution
- undertake tests on goodness-of-fit
- undertake tests on contingency tables.

The χ^2 distribution

We state that the distribution has a PDF of the form:

$$f(x) \quad = A_\nu \left(\frac{x}{2}\right)^{\frac{\nu}{2}-1} e^{-\frac{x}{2}} \text{ for } x > 0$$

where A is a constant dependent on ν and ν is an integral parameter known as the number of degrees of freedom of the distribution. (ν is another Greek letter, nu, pronounced 'new'.) You do not need to understand the meaning of A, and ν will be explained as we use it.

Figure 4.1 illustrates the nature of the PDF for certain values of ν.

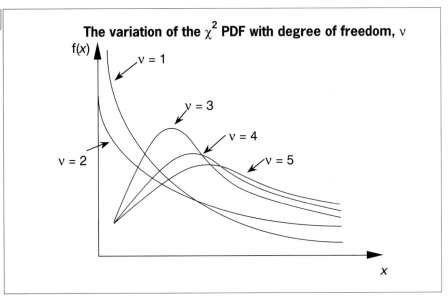

Figure 4.1

The variation of the χ^2 PDF with degree of freedom, ν

You may well have appreciated from the PDF that the direct calculation of a χ^2 probability is not a prospect to look forward to. However, as with the normal distribution, we will not be required to perform such calculations, since we can obtain these probabilities from the χ^2 table (see Appendix 3 at the end of the book).

We will now look at several examples whose general theme is as follows: given some data we have collected, how well does it correspond to one of our theoretical distributions? This type of test is called a **goodness-of-fit test** and makes use of the χ^2 distribution.

The discrete uniform distribution

Consider the following situation. You have been involved in a game of chance involving gambling. The game involved rolling the usual six-sided die and betting on the outcome (i.e. which of the six numbers showed). You have lost a considerable sum of money and are wondering if the die is actually a fair one. To test this out you have borrowed the die and rolled it 150 times with the following results:

Table 4.1	Outcomes for die
Number showing	*Frequency*
1	23
2	20
3	27
4	26
5	22
6	32
Total	150

The question we would like an answer to is: 'Based on the evidence, is the die a fair one?' The χ^2 test provides us with an answer to the question.

We could argue that we would normally expect an exactly equal distribution given that each number ought to have a one in six chance of showing on each throw. But we also know that such a probability is strictly a long-term average and there remains the question as to whether 150 throws is sufficient. Perhaps if we threw another 150 times the frequencies might begin to balance themselves out more.

It is clear that what we require is some formal method of determining whether the data we have obtained follows an approximately uniform distribution as we would expect. We follow a similar process to the other tests we have examined. Our null hypothesis and alternative hypothesis are:

H_0 :   The data follows a uniform distribution.

H_1 :   The data follows a distribution which is not uniform.

Under H_0 we can work out frequencies which we would expect to get and these are shown in Table 4.2.

Table 4.2	Showing observed and expected frequencies	
Number showing	*Observed frequency (O)*	*Expected frequency (E)*
1	23	25
2	20	25
3	27	25
4	26	25
5	22	25
6	32	25
Total	150	150

Effectively the null hypothesis is that the observed and expected frequencies are not different.

We now work out the quantity:

$$\sum \frac{(O-E)^2}{E}$$

which is called the χ^2 statistic

It can be shown (but is not required at 'A' level) that:

$$\sum \frac{(O-E)^2}{E} \sim \chi^2(v)$$

where v is the number of **degrees of freedom** of the distribution.

The complete calculation for this example is shown in Table 4.3.

Table 4.3   Calculation of χ^2 for the data

Number showing	Observed frequency	Expected frequency	$(O-E)$	$(O-E)^2$	$\dfrac{(O-E)^2}{E}$
1	23	25	−2	4	0.16
2	20	25	−5	25	1
3	27	25	2	4	0.16
4	26	25	1	1	0.04
5	22	25	−3	9	0.36
6	32	25	7	49	1.96
Total	150	150	0		3.68

So we have $\sum \dfrac{(O-E)^2}{E} = 3.68$

To find the number of degrees of freedom for this and subsequent tests:

- count up the number of cells (or values that have been compared) which in this case is six

- subtract 1, as in this example only five frequencies are actually independent – if we knew five of the frequencies we could work out the sixth, since the total must be 150

- subtract from this the number of parameters that have been estimated using the data

i.e. $v = k - s - 1$

where k = the number of cells

        s = the number of parameters estimated from the data.

In this example we have not used the data to estimate any parameters and so $s = 0$ and $v = k - 1 = 6 - 1 = 5$

Hence our statistic $\sum \dfrac{(O-E)^2}{E} \sim \chi^2(5)$ in this example.

Recall from Section 3 that we need to fix a level of significance for an hypothesis test. Here, and throughout this section, we will consider only 5% levels and all the tests will be one-tailed, i.e. we reject H_0 if our test statistic (χ^2) lies in a region shown in Figure 4.2.

Figure 4.2

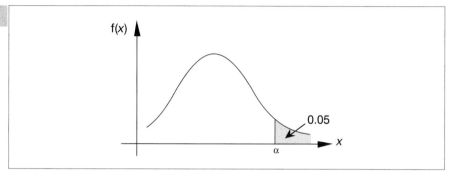

i.e. we will reject H_0 if our calculated value lies to the right of α, as shown. It is precisely the value of α that is given in the χ^2 distribution table in Appendix 3 at the end of the book.

Turning now to the table we see that in this example where $v = 5$ (v is given in the left-hand column) and with significance level of 0.05 (given in the top row of the table):

● the tabulated value of $\chi^2(5)$ is 11.070 (the critical value) – we will abbreviate this in future to $\chi^2_{5\%}(5)$

● our calculated value was 3.68 – our abbreviation for this is $\chi^2_{calc}(5)$.

Since $\chi^2_{calc}(5) < \chi^2_{5\%}(5)$

we conclude that H_0 should be accepted and that the uniform distribution provides a good model for the data given (at the 5% level of significance).

For tests with other significance levels (e.g. 1%) the procedure is exactly the same except for the value looked up in tables for comparison with the value of $\chi^2_{calc}(5)$, e.g. in this example if we had been conducting a test at the 1% level then we would have compared our value of 3.68 with the tabulated value of 15.086 to be found in the same row but now under the column headed 0.010.

The next example shows the amount of work required for a χ^2 test.

Example   The number of books borrowed from a library during a given week was 135 on Monday, 108 on Tuesday, 120 on Wednesday, 114 on Thursday and 148 on Friday. Is there any evidence at the 5% level of significance that the number of books borrowed depends on the day of the week?

Solution H_0 :   The number of books borrowed is independent of the day of the week (i.e. data is uniform).

H_1 :   The number of books borrowed is dependent on the day of the week (i.e. data is non-uniform).

Test at 5% significance level (one-tailed).

Table 4.4

0	E	0 – E	(0 – E)²	$\dfrac{(0 - E)^2}{E}$
135	125	10	100	0.800
108	125	–17	289	2.312
120	125	–5	25	0.200
114	125	–11	121	0.968
148	125	23	529	4.232
Total 625	625	0		8.512

Number of degrees of freedom = 5 – 1 = 4 (no parameters calculated from the data and the totals must agree)

$$\chi^2_{calc}(4) = 8.512$$

From the table in Appendix 3, we see

$$\chi^2_{5\%}(4) = 9.488$$

Since $\chi^2_{calc}(4) < \chi^2_{5\%}(4)$,

we accept H_0.

We conclude that there is no significant difference between the observed data and a uniform distribution.

The binomial distribution

Our next example deals with testing a hypothesis about possible bias in jury selection.

Example   It is known that 55% of potential jurors are female. A random sample of 150 juries gave the distribution shown in Table 4.5.

Does this data approximate to a binomial distribution $X \sim B(150, 0.55)$ or is there some gender bias in the way that juries are selected?

Table 4.5   Selection of female jurors

Number of females on the jury	Number of trials
0	0
1	0
2	2
3	6
4	14
5	25
6	30
7	32
8	24
9	10
10	7
11	0
12	0
Total	150

Solution   We set up two hypotheses:

H_0 : the data comes from the binomial distribution $X \sim B(150, 0.55)$

H_1 : the data does not come from a binomial distribution
        (but from some other distribution)

In order to apply the χ^2 test to this data, we first need to calculate the expected frequencies under the null hypothesis that the data is binomial, with $P = 0.55$.

For $X \sim B(150, 0.55)$, $P(X = 0) = (0.45)^{12}$

$P(X = 1) = {}^{12}C_1 (0.45)^{11} (0.55)$

$P(X = 2) = {}^{12}C_2 (0.45)^{10} (0.55)^2$ and so on

To be able to compare these with the frequencies in Table 4.5, we need to find the corresponding proportions (out of 150) and so each probability must be multiplied by 150.

Completing this process gives Table 4.6.

Table 4.6   Selection of jurors, with expected values

Number of females on the jury	O	E
0	0	0.01
1	0	0.15
2	2	1.02
3	6	4.15
4	14	11.43
5	25	22.34
6	30	31.86
7	32	33.38
8	24	25.50
9	10	13.84
10	7	5.08
11	0	1.13
12	0	0.11
Total	150	150

At this point it is important to notice that some of the values of E are less than 5 (this didn't occur in the previous examples). In such circumstances we have to combine cells with adjacent ones until each value for E is ≥ 5.

This process is referred to as 'pooling' classes.

This process produces Table 4.7 where the cells for 0, 1, 2 and 3 have been combined and cells for 10, 11 and 12 have been combined. Once this has been done we can then proceed with the test and calculate $\dfrac{(O-E)^2}{E}$ as has been done in the last column.

Table 4.7   Complete jury selection calculations

Number of females on the jury	O	E	$\dfrac{(O-E)^2}{E}$
≤ 3	8	5.33	1.34
4	14	11.43	0.58
5	25	22.34	0.32
6	30	31.86	0.11
7	32	33.38	0.06
8	24	25.50	0.06
9	10	13.84	1.07
≥ 10	7	6.22	0.10
Total	150	150.00	3.64

The degrees of freedom for the test are based on the amalgamated table giving

$v = 8 - 0 - 1$ (since no parameters have been calculated from the data)

i.e. $v = 7$

With $\alpha = 0.05$, we have from the table that $\chi^2_{5\%}(7) = 14.067$ and since $\chi^2_{calc}(7) = 3.64$, we conclude that the null hypothesis should be accepted at the 5% level of significance, i.e. based on the evidence, there is no significant gender bias in selecting juries.

Fitting a Poisson distribution

The procedure for testing data against some assumed Poisson distribution is similar to that for a binomial. However, we will use this as a means of illustrating another common feature of such examples (and examination questions). With the binomial example we were given the parameters of the assumed distribution. Often we are required to derive them directly from the data itself.

Example   An engineer has been studying the Poisson distribution, and feels it would be very useful in her current situation where the frequency of breakdown of a particular type of machine is being examined. For the machine type under consideration the following data has been collected:

Table 4.8   Machine breakdowns

Number of breakdowns in a given hour	Frequency
0	50
1	125
2	140
3	105
4	55
5	35
6	17
7	8
Total	535

$\dfrac{4389}{535} - 2 \cdot 38^2$

$\sigma^2 = 2 \cdot 5$

We pose the question: does this data follow a Poisson process?

Solution   In order to apply the χ^2 test we require expected frequencies derived using Poisson probabilities. But to calculate such probabilities, we require a value for μ, the average value.

Using the standard approach for calculating the mean of a frequency distribution we have:

$$\Sigma fx = 1273$$
$$\Sigma f = 535$$
$$\bar{x} = \frac{1273}{535} = 2.38 \qquad 2.4$$

i.e. the average number of breakdowns per hour is 2.38.

Using this as the value for μ we can now proceed to determine the Poisson probability for each of the breakdown values, determine the expected frequencies, and then perform the test itself.

The appropriate hypotheses are:

H_0 : The data comes from the Poisson distribution, $X \sim P(2.38)$
H_1 : The data does not come from a Poisson distribution

Expected number with 0 breakdowns

$$= e^{-2.38} \times 535 \qquad = 49.5$$

Expected number with 1 breakdown

$$= e^{-2.38} \frac{2.38^1}{1!} \times 535 \qquad = 117.8$$

Expected number with 2 breakdowns

$$= e^{-2.38} \frac{2.38^2}{2!} \times 535 \qquad = 140.2$$

Expected number with 3 breakdowns

$$= e^{-2.38} \frac{2.38^3}{3!} \times 535 \qquad = 111.3$$

Similar calculations give:

4 breakdowns = 66.2
5 breakdowns = 31.5
6 breakdowns = 12.5
7 breakdowns = 4.2

If we sum these values we get 533.2 and the difference arises because the theoretical Poisson distribution which is modelling the data can actually take values greater than 7, albeit with small probabilities. To take account of this, we calculate the final cell by making the totals agree. This produces Table 4.9.

Table 4.9

Number of breakdowns	O	E
0	50	49.5
1	125	117.8
2	140	140.2
3	105	111.3
4	55	66.2
5	35	31.5
6	17	12.5
7 or more	8	6.0
Total	535	535.0

We now check that no pooling of cells is required (there are no E-values less than 5).

The number of degrees of freedom for the test is $8 - 1 - 1 = 6$, since we have used the data to find one parameter and the totals must agree.

$$\chi^2_{calc}(6) = \frac{0.5^2}{49.5} + \frac{7.2^2}{117.8} + \frac{0.2^2}{140.2} + \dots + \frac{4.5^2}{12.5} + \frac{2.0^2}{6.0} = 5.4$$

$$\chi^2_{5\%}(6) = 12.59 \text{ at 5\% level of significance}$$

and so $\chi^2_{calc}(6) < \chi^2_{5\%}(6)$.

We conclude that at the 5% significance level, there is no evidence to suggest that H_0 should be rejected.

For practical purposes it is worth noting that an important property of the Poisson distribution (and therefore any data that should be modelled by it) is that the mean and variance are the same. As a preliminary therefore, before conducting the χ^2 test, it is worth calculating values for the sample mean and the sample variance – if these are found to be very different then the Poisson distribution is unlikely to be a useful model for the data.

Fitting a normal distribution

This type of test will be dealt with in detail as there are important differences when the model is continuous and defined over a sample space which is infinite.

Consider the following continuous data which relates to the heights of a sample of a certain variety of shrub 3 weeks after planting.

Height (cm)	0–5	6–10	11–15	16–20	21–25	26–30	More than 31
Number of shrubs	13	21	42	63	38	16	7

The heights are recorded to the nearest centimetre and so for example the interval 6–10 means any height satisfying $5.5 \leq x < 10.5$ would be placed in that interval.

Using these true class boundaries we can calculate the sample mean and sample variance from Table 4.10

Table 4.10

Height	Frequency	Class boundaries	Mid point	$f \times x$	$f \times x^2$
0–5	13	$0 \leq x \leq 5.5$	2.75	35.75	98.3125
6–10	21	$5.5 \leq x < 10.5$	8	168	1344
11–15	42	$10.5 \leq x < 15.5$	13	546	7098
16–20	63	$15.5 \leq x < 20.5$	18	1134	20412
21–25	38	$20.5 \leq x < 25.5$	23	874	20102
26–30	16	$25.5 \leq x < 30.5$	28	448	12544
More than 31	7	$30.5 \leq x$	33	231	7623
	200			3436.75	69221.3125

(where the mid-point for the final interval was based on interval width the same as the others.)

We get $\quad \bar{x} = 17.184$ (3 d.p.)

$$s^2 = \left(\frac{69\,221.3125}{200} - (17.184)^2 \right) \times \frac{200}{199}$$

$$= 51.081 \ (3 \text{ d.p.})$$

with these preliminaries completed we will now continue with the χ^2 test.

$\quad H_0$: The data comes from a normal distribution

$\quad H_1$: The data comes from a distribution which is not normal.

one-tailed test

5% level of significance.

parameters calculated from the data $\quad \bar{x} = 17.184$

$\hspace{9.5cm} s^2 = 51.081$

In order to calculate the expected frequencies under the null hypothesis we now have to find, for the distribution $X \sim N(17.184, 51.081)$ the following probabilities

$\quad P(X < 5.5)$ (since the model extends to $-\infty$)

$\quad P(5.5 \leq X < 10.5)$

$\quad P(10.5 \leq X < 15.5)$ etc.

to $\quad P(X \geq 30.5)$

and it will be these when multiplied up by the factor 200 which will be compared with the observed frequencies.

The calculations are set out in detail below.

Table 4.11

Height	z-value	probability (P)	E(= P × 200)
< 5.5	$z < -1.635$	0.051	10.22
$5.5 \leq x < 10.5$	$-1.635 \leq z < -0.935$	0.124	24.8
$10.5 \leq x < 15.5$	$-0.935 \leq z < -0.236$	0.228	45.6
$15.5 \leq x < 20.5$	$-0.236 \leq z < 0.464$	0.271	54.2
$20.5 \leq x < 25.5$	$0.464 \leq z < 1.164$	0.199	39.8
$25.5 \leq x < 30.5$	$1.164 \leq z < 1.863$	0.091	18.2
$x \geq 30.5$	$z \geq 1.863$	0.0313	6.3
		0.9953	199.12

With practice you will find that these calculations can be completed fairly quickly as the endpoint of one interval is effectively the beginning of another.

To illustrate how the z-numbers are obtained consider the interval $15.5 \leq x < 20.5$.

We are using $X \sim N(17.184, 7.15^2)$ as the model and require $P(15.5 \leq X < 20.5)$.

With the usual standardising procedure this leads to

$$P\left(\frac{15.5 - 17.184}{7.15} \leq z < \frac{20.5 - 17.184}{7.15}\right)$$

$$= P(-0.236 \leq z < 0.464) \text{ rounded to 3 d.p.}$$

Tables (with linear interpolation as necessary) are then used to calculate the final probability. The discrepancy in the totals is due to the rounding which was necessary in the calculations and to make our E-values total exactly to 200 we will adjust the first and last values by an amount of 0.06 to make the match exact. These intervals are chosen as they are less well defined than the intervening ones.

Our table for the χ^2 test now is as follows:

Table 4.12

Height	O	E	$\dfrac{(O-E)^2}{E}$
0–5	13	10.66	0.5137
6–10	21	24.8	0.5823
11–15	42	45.6	0.2842
16–20	63	54.2	1.4288
21–25	38	39.8	0.0814
26–30	16	18.2	0.2659
More than 31	7	6.74	0.0192
TOTALS	200	200	3.1755

$v = 7 - 2 - 1 = 4$ (since we have 7 cells and 2 parameters were calculated from the data)

Hence

$$\chi^2_{calc}\,(4) \;=\; 3.2025$$

From the χ^2 distribution table,

$$\chi^2_{5\%}\,(4) = 9.488$$

and since $\chi^2_{calc}\,(4) < \chi^2_{5\%}\,(4)$

we calculate that the normal distribution is a good model for the data.

Fitting a continuous uniform distribution

The following data is thought to come from a continuous uniform distribution (where x is measured to the nearest whole number).

x	0–5	6–10	11–15	16–20	21–25	26–30
f	4	12	14	13	6	5

Test this claim at the 5% level.

If the uniform distribution is appropriate then each frequency should be the same, i.e. we would expect each to be 9 (54 ÷ 6), giving the following table:

O	E	$\dfrac{(O-E)^2}{E}$
4	9	$\dfrac{25}{9}$
12	9	$\dfrac{9}{9}$
14	9	$\dfrac{25}{9}$
13	9	$\dfrac{16}{9}$
6	9	$\dfrac{9}{9}$
5	9	$\dfrac{16}{9}$
		$\dfrac{100}{9}$

$v = 6 - 1 = 5$ (since no parameters were required).

$$\chi^2_{calc}(5) = \frac{100}{9} = 11.11$$

From the table in Appendix 3,

$$\chi^2_{5\%}(5) = 11.07$$

and since $\chi^2_{calc}(5) > \chi^2_{5\%}(5)$

we conclude that at a 5% level of significance the null hypothesis should be rejected and the uniform distribution does not provide a good model for the data.

In these circumstances it may be appropriate to consider whether the normal distribution fits the data better. This is set as an exercise at the end of this section.

Contingency tables

As well as being used to test goodness-of-fit, the χ^2 test can be applied to a particular type of table known as a contingency table.

Frequently, we may be analysing data that can be classed by two (or more) attributes. Let us remain with the last example.

Example	Assume that we had collected data on the number of students who fell into each of the pass/fail categories for each sex, male and female.

Table 4.13   Examination results by sex

Sex	Pass	Fail	Total
Male	90	30	120
Female	55	25	80
Total	145	55	200

We wish to establish whether a student's sex has had any effect on whether they passed or failed the exam. Effectively we wish to determine whether the two factors are statistically independent of each other, or whether one is contingent (hence the name of the test) upon the other.

Solution	The steps of the test are similar to those of the goodness-of-fit test covered earlier with the exception of the way in which we determine the expected frequencies. Our null hypothesis is that the two factors are independent.

Formally

H_0 : exam results and gender are independent attributes

H_1 : exam result is dependent on gender

If this is the case then (from the basic rules of probability) we have:

$$P(\text{Male} \cap \text{Pass}) = P(\text{Male}) \times P(\text{Pass})$$
$$= \frac{120}{200} \times \frac{145}{200} = 0.435$$

and given that there are 200 students we would expect 87 students that is, 200×0.435, to fall into this particular category, assuming that the null hypothesis is correct.

Continuing in this way:

$$P(\text{Male} \cap \text{Fail}) = \frac{33}{200} \qquad \text{expected frequency} = 33$$

$$P(\text{Female} \cap \text{Pass}) = \frac{58}{200} \qquad \text{expected frequency} = 58$$

$$P(\text{Female} \cap \text{Fail}) = \frac{22}{200} \qquad \text{expected frequency} = 22$$

Note that the totals of the expected frequencies are the same as the actual totals shown in the table.

The number of degrees of freedom for such a test is determined as follows. We have a 2×2 table (ignoring the totals) and therefore require four expected values. Given the need to balance rows and columns against the given totals it is clear that once we have calculated one expected value the rest must be determined. This gives one degree of freedom.

In situations where there is one degree of freedom, it is necessary to modify the calculation of χ^2 slightly.

The value of χ^2 is worked out by :

$$\chi^2 = \frac{\Sigma(\,|\,O-E\,|\,-0.5)^2}{E}$$

and this is similar to the continuity correction from Module T1. It is known as **Yates' correction** and should always be used for a 2×2 contingency table.

We can now proceed to calculate the χ^2 statistic and undertake the rest of the test.

The separate tables are as follows:

Observed

90	30
55	25

Expected

87	33
58	22

For the values of observed = 90 and expected = 87, we would get the term:

$$\frac{(\,|\,90-87\,|\,-0.5)^2}{80} = \frac{2.5^2}{80}$$

and for observed = 30, expected = 33, we get:

$$\frac{(\,|\,30-33\,|\,-0.5)^2}{33} = \frac{2.5^2}{33}$$

Similar calculations for the remaining pairs give:

$$\chi^2_{calc} = \frac{2.5^2}{87} + \frac{2.5^2}{33} + \frac{2.5^2}{58} + \frac{2.5^2}{22} = 0.653$$

So $\quad \chi^2_{calc}(1) = 0.653$

From tables, $\quad \chi^2_{5\%}(1) = 3.841$ at the 5% level

Since $\quad \chi^2_{calc}(1) < \chi^2_{5\%}(1)$

we accept H_0 at the 5% level and conclude that there is no evidence of dependence between a student's gender and whether they pass or fail.

The test is easily extended to larger contingency tables; the principles remain exactly the same. In general the degrees of freedom will be obtained by:

$$v = (r - 1) \times (c - 1)$$

where r is the number of rows in the table (excluding totals)

             c is the number of columns (again excluding totals)

and where Yates' correction is not necessary.

Example   A random sample of 100 people were asked by a market research team whether or not they had ever used Sudsey soap. 58 said 'yes' and 42 said 'no'. In a second sample of 80, 62 said 'yes' and 18 said 'no'. A third sample of 75 gave 46 'yes' replies and 29 'no' replies.

Are these three samples showing consistent replies?

Solution H_0 : The proportion of 'yes' responses is independent of the sample

H_1 : The proportion of 'yes' responses depends on which sample you choose.

Observed

	1st	2nd	3rd	Total
Yes	58	62	46	166
No	42	18	29	89
Total	100	80	75	255

Expected

	1st	2nd	3rd	Total
Yes	65.1	52.1	48.8	166
No	34.9	27.9	26.2	89
Total	100	80	75	255

(where for example $\dfrac{100 \times 166}{255}$ gives the reading of 65.1 in the expected box and the remaining calculations are done similarly)

$v = (2 - 1) \times (3 - 1) = 2$

$$\chi^2_{calc} (2) \quad = \frac{(58 - 65.1)^2}{65.1} + \frac{(62 - 52.1)^2}{52.1} + \frac{(46 - 48.8)^2}{48.8}$$

$$+ \frac{(42 - 34.9)^2}{34.9} + \frac{(18 - 27.9)^2}{27.9} + \frac{(29 - 26.2)^2}{26.2}$$

$$= 8.073$$

From tables $\chi^2_{5\%} (2) = 5.991$

and we are over this, so we reject H_0.

You should now be able to answer Exercises 1–10 on pages 65–68.

PROJECT EXERCISES

1   Waiting times in queues would be expected to follow a distribution called the exponential distribution. Time yourself in several queues and find a reference to the exponential distribution (not officially within the syllabus – but an important distribution nevertheless). Determine whether the waiting times do indeed follow this type of distribution.

2   Use the data obtained in Project exercise 2 from Section 3 to determine whether errors in estimating lengths or times follow a normal distribution.

3   If a coin is fair then the number of heads obtained in 10 throws should follow a binomial distribution $B(10, \frac{1}{2})$. By repeating this experiment (i.e. 10 throws) many times and counting the number of heads out of 10 each time, test the fairness of the coin.

EXERCISES

1 A calibrated instrument is used over a wide range of values. To assess the operator's ability to read the instrument accurately, the final digit in each of 700 readings was noted. The results are tabulated below.

Final digit	0	1	2	3	4	5	6	7	8	9
Frequency	75	63	50	58	73	95	96	63	46	81

Use an approximate χ^2 statistic to test whether there is any evidence of bias in the operator's reading of the instrument. Use a 5% significance level and state your null and alternative hypotheses.

2 A market researcher interested in assessing the demand for a new product, advertised the product on local radio for five consecutive days. A telephone number was given so that potential customers could make contact and gain further information.

The results obtained are summarised below.

Day	Mon	Tues	Wed	Thurs	Fri
Number of calls	41	31	44	57	55

Stating clearly your hypotheses and using a 5% level of significance, test whether or not the number of calls received is independent of the day of the week.

3 The following table shows the number of girls in families of 4 children:

Number of girls	0	1	2	3	4
Frequency	15	68	69	38	10

A researcher suggests that a binomial distribution with $n = 4$ and $p = 0.5$ could be a suitable model for the number of girls in a family of 4 children

(a) Test the researcher's suggestion at the 5% level, stating your null and alternative hypotheses clearly.

The research decides to progress to a more refined model and retains the idea of a binomial distribution, but does not specify the value of p, the probability that the child is a girl.

(b) Use the data in the table to estimate p.

The researcher used the value of p in (b) and the refined model, to obtain expected frequencies and found $\sum \dfrac{(O - E)^2}{E} = 2.47$.

(There was no pooling of classes.)

(c) Test, at the 5% level, whether the binomial distribution is a suitable model of the number of girls in a family of 4 children.

(d) A family planning clinic has a large number of enquiries from families with 3 boys who would like a fourth child in the hope of having a girl, but they believe their chances are very small. What advice can the researcher give on the basis of the above tests?

4 During hockey practice, each member of a squad of 60 players attempted to hit a ball between two posts. Each player had 8 attempts and the numbers of successes were as follows:

3 4 8 1 0 3 3 4 4 2 6 7 3 2 2 5 5 5 8 1 3 5 6 1 3 4 4 4 1 0

5 3 6 0 6 7 4 3 5 7 0 1 2 6 1 8 0 0 3 0 4 4 1 3 5 0 8 1 8 8

(a) Form the data into an ungrouped frequency distribution.

(b) Use the χ^2 distribution at the 5% significance level to test whether the binomial distribution is an adequate model for the data.

(c) State, giving a reason, whether the data support the view that the probability of success is the same for each player.

[AEB]

5 The number of flaws per 20 metres of a cotton fabric were counted and gave the following frequencies.

Number of flaws	0	1	2	3	4	5	6 or more
frequency	3	7	11	4	5	3	4

Are the data consistent with a Poisson distribution? Test at 5% and 1% significance levels.

6 The following table gives the masses (to the nearest gram) of some items from a factory production line.

Mass (g)	< 995	995–997	998–1000	1001–1004	1005–1007	1008–1010	> 1010
Frequency	2	8	15	32	51	27	18

Is the data consistent with the normal distribution at a 5% significance level?

7 For the data given at the bottom of page 60, determine whether the normal distribution provides a better model for the given data.

8 The following table is the result of analysing a random sample of the invoices submitted by branches of a large chain of bookshops.

	Novel	Textbook	General interest
Hardback	24	10	22
Paperback	66	10	18

Using an approximate χ^2 statistic, assess, at the 5% level of significance, whether or not there is any association between the type of book sold and its cover.

State clearly your null and alternative hypotheses.

9 Two schools enter their pupils for a particular public examination and the results obtained are shown below.

	Credit	Pass	Fail
School *A*	51	10	19
School *B*	39	10	21

By using an approximate χ^2 statistic, assess at the 5% level of significance, whether or not there is a significant difference between the two schools with respect to the proportions of pupils in the three grades. State your null and alternative hypotheses.

10 (a) Some years ago a Polytechnic decided to require all entrants to a science course to study a non-science subject for one year. In the first year of the scheme entrants were given the choice of studying French or Russian. The number of students of each sex choosing each language is shown in the following table:

	French	Russian
Male	39	16
Female	21	14

Use a χ^2 test (including Yates' correction) at the 5% significance level to test whether choice of language is independent of sex.

(b) The choice of non-science subjects has now been widened and the current figures are as follows:

	French	Poetry	Russian	Sculpture
Male	2	8	15	10
Female	10	17	21	37

Use a χ^2 test at the 5% significance level to test whether choice of subject is independent of sex. In applying the test you should combine French with another subject. Explain why this is necessary and the reasons for your choice.

(c) Point out two features of the data (other than the increase in the number of options and in the total number of students) which have changed markedly over the years.

[AEB]

SUMMARY   Now you have completed this section you will appreciate that:

- the χ^2 test is a method of comparing data with probability distributions
- expected frequencies less than 5 should be pooled
- the χ^2 test can also be used to test for independence of attributes in a contingency table
- Yates' correction should be used when the number of degrees of freedom is 1.

5

Correlation

Our methods so far have been confined to a single variable (univariate data), but many situations arise where we might want to investigate whether there is a relationship between two (or more) variables. In Sections 5 and 6 we will be concerned with the possible links between two variables (bivariate data)

By the end of this section you should be able to:

- plot and interpret a scatter diagram
- calculate and interpret the product moment correlation
- calculate and interpret Spearman's rank correlation coefficient
- be aware of the limitations of the coefficients.

Scatter diagrams

Consider the data in Table 5.1

Table 5.1

Item	Height (cm)	Weight (kg)
1	158.8	48.9
2	172.1	100.7
3	154.8	37.2
4	172.8	90.4
5	172.9	88.1
6	168.8	80.7
7	171.3	79.6
8	159.9	68.1
9	162.8	53.2
10	164.8	65.0

We would like to know whether a relationship exists between the two variables, height and weight. Common sense suggests that there might be, but we would like more evidence than just our intuitive feelings about the situation. A good rough and ready way is to plot the data in graphical form and we do this by considering each item to be an ordered pair and then plotting the graph in the normal way. This is shown in Figure 5.1 and is called a scatter diagram.

Assume that for ten adult females (numbered 1–10) we have measured their height (in cm) and their weight (in kg). So each item has two measurements associated with it: we call this a **bivariate** situation.

Figure 5.1

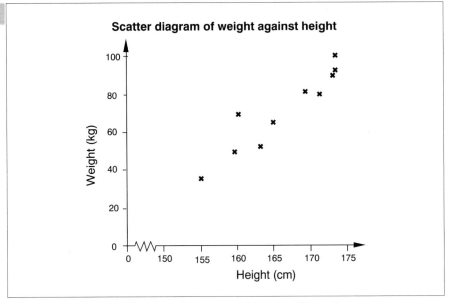

Scatter diagram of weight against height

There are a number of points that we could make about the picture:

- It is important to choose scales and axes so that the data is clearly shown. It would not be sensible in this example to start the axis at zero.

- The two variables appear to increase together: larger values for height seem to be associated with larger values for weight.

- There is a suggestion of some sort of linear relationship between the two variables.

In Figure 5.2 some further common types of scatter diagrams are shown.

Figure 5.2

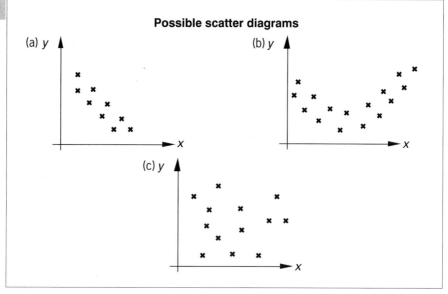

Possible scatter diagrams

(a) *y*

(b) *y*

(c) *y*

A possible interpretation of each of these might be

(a)   perhaps a linear relationship between *x* and *y*, but with *y* decreasing as *x* increases (i.e. negative gradient)

(b)   not a linear relationship, but possibly a quadratic one between *x* and *y* (i.e. *y* is possibly some quadratic function of *x*). In this module we are only concerned with linear relationships (although it is possible to transform from non-linear to linear relationships by using logarithms or changes of variable). In the case of the quadratic relationship $y = kx^2$ there would be a linear relationship between $Y = y$ and $X = x^2$.

(c)   no relationship observable.

Product moment correlation coefficient

The scatter diagram gives a good general impression of the data and will usually be the first step in interpreting it. It is also valuable to have a numerical measure of the degree of linearity of the relationship – this is provided by the **product moment correlation coefficient** (usually referred to more simply as the correlation coefficient).

The derivation of the expression for the correlation coefficient is not required for 'A' level, but it is instructive to have a fairly general idea of how it is constructed.

If we write:

$$S_{xx} = \Sigma(x_i - \bar{x})^2$$

We can think of S_{xx} as the sum of the squared deviations of the x-values from their mean value.

In a similar way we could write

$$S_{yy} = \Sigma(y_i - \bar{y})^2$$

where S_{yy} by analogy means the sum of the squared deviations of the y-values from their mean.

We write

$$S_{xy} = \Sigma(x_i - \bar{x})(y_i - \bar{y})$$

for the product of the deviations of x and y from their respective means.

Note that $\dfrac{S_{xx}}{n}$ and $\dfrac{S_{yy}}{n}$ would give expressions corresponding to the biased sample variances of the x-values and the y-values respectively (we would need to multiply each of these by $\dfrac{n}{n-1}$ to give the unbiased values as we saw earlier). Corresponding to this we call the quantity $\dfrac{S_{xy}}{n}$ the **covariance** of x and y. This quantity will take positive or negative values according to whether the values of (x_i, y_i) are in the regions shown in Figure 5.3.

Figure 5.3

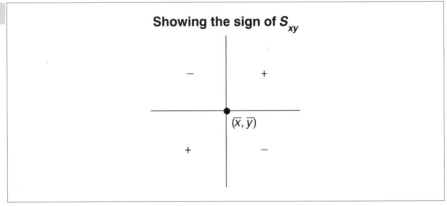

Showing the sign of S_{xy}

Therefore if the data lies predominantly in the two quadrants marked with +, then S_{xy} will itself be positive and vice versa. If there is a random scattering of points throughout all four quadrants then the positive contributions to their sum will tend to cancel out the negative contributions leading to an approximately zero value for S_{xy}. The correlation coefficient is defined by the formula:

$$r = \frac{S_{xy}}{\sqrt{S_{xx} \cdot S_{yy}}}$$

The statistic r is an estimate for the corresponding population correlation coefficient which is usually given the symbol ρ (the Greek letter rho).

The reason for the denominator in this expression is to make r free of units. It also gives r the important property that:

$$-1 \le r \le 1$$

The value of r would equal 1 if our data lay on a perfect straight line with positive gradient and this would be referred to as **perfect positive correlation**.

A value of $r = -1$ would correspond to data points exactly on a line with negative gradient, referred to as **perfect negative correlation**. A value of $r = 0$ would correspond to data which was **uncorrelated**.

In statistical studies we are likely to find values of r between these extremes and we need to be able to give an interpretation of these. Before dealing with this problem it is worth the effort to arrive at a modified but equivalent version of the formula for r – one which will be simpler to use in practice.

Calculating r in practice

The expression for S_{xy} , although useful for the derivation of an expression for r, is rather cumbersome to use and as with many other statistical formulae we can produce a version which cuts calculation time considerably.

$$
\begin{aligned}
S_{xy} &= \Sigma(x_i - \bar{x})(y_i - \bar{y}) \\
&= (x_1 - \bar{x})(y_1 - \bar{y}) + (x_2 - \bar{x})(y_2 - \bar{y}) + \dots + (x_n - \bar{x})(y_n - \bar{y}) \\
&= (x_1 y_1 - y_1\bar{x} - x_1\bar{y} + \bar{x}\bar{y}) + (x_2 y_2 - \bar{x}y_2 - \bar{y}x_2 + \bar{x}\bar{y}) \\
&\quad + \dots + (x_n y_n - \bar{x}y_n - \bar{y}x_n + \bar{x}\bar{y}) \\
&= (x_1 y_1 + x_2 y_2 + \dots + x_n y_n) \\
&\quad - \bar{x}(y_1 + y_2 + \dots + y_n) - \bar{y}(x_1 + x_2 + \dots + x_n) + n\bar{x}\bar{y} \\
&= \Sigma x_i y_i - \bar{x}n\bar{y} - \bar{y}n\bar{x} + n\bar{x}\bar{y}
\end{aligned}
$$

(using the fact that $y_1 + y_2 + \dots + y_n = n\bar{y}$)

$$= \Sigma x_i y_i - n\bar{x}\bar{y}$$

This is much easier to use. We can also use results from earlier for S_{xx} and S_{yy} namely

$$S_{xx} = \Sigma x_i^2 - n\bar{x}^2$$
$$S_{yy} = \Sigma y_i^2 - n\bar{y}^2$$

Collecting together these various expressions produces

$$r = \frac{\Sigma\, x_i y_i - n\bar{x}\,\bar{y}}{\sqrt{(\Sigma x_i^2 - n\bar{x}^2)\,(\Sigma y_i^2 - n\bar{y}^2)}}$$

which is the version we will use for actual calculations.

Example   As an illustration of the use of this formula consider the (unlikely) set of data

x_i	y_i
2	5
3	7
4	9
5	11

Find the correlation coefficient.

Solution   We set out the solution in a table is shown

	x_i	y_i	x_i^2	y_i^2	$x_i y_i$
	2	5	4	25	10
	3	7	9	49	21
	4	9	16	81	36
	5	11	25	121	55
Totals	14	32	54	276	122

$\bar{x} = 3.5$

$\bar{y} = 8$

$$r = \frac{122 - (4)\,(3.5)\,(8)}{\sqrt{(54 - 49)\,(276 - 256)}}$$

$$= \frac{10}{\sqrt{5 \times 20}} = \frac{10}{10} = 1$$

This result should not be a surprise – the data was especially chosen to exhibit perfect positive correlation and this has been confirmed by the value of r.

You should now be able to answer Exercises 1–3 on pages 82–83.

Rank correlation

In some circumstances, it is not necessarily the values of x_i and y_i which may be of interest, but only the relative orders of them.

Example

Suppose that two judges A and B at a flower show award points out of 10 to six exhibits according to the following scheme

	1	2	3	4	5	6
A	8	3	9	5	0	7
B	9	2	8	7	4	3

Are the judges showing any similarity in their assessments of the merits of the exhibits?

Solution

The actual values of the marks given are not particularly significant here. What is more significant is the order in which they have placed the exhibits.

For this data we will calculate **Spearman's Rank correlation coefficient**, a statistic which is virtually identical to the correlation coefficient, but which operates on ranks rather than actual data. The formula for the statistic is shown below.

Spearman's Rank correlation coefficient

$$r_s = 1 - \frac{6\Sigma d^2}{n(n^2 - 1)}$$

---

where d will be explained as we go, and n is the number of pairs of data.

The derivation r_s is identical to that of r except that ranks are used instead. Its derivation assumes that no ranks are 'tied', i.e. in the example above that neither judge gives exactly the same marks for two exhibits. In cases where tied ranks are observed it would be necessary to use the formula for r on the ranks rather than the simpler r_s. To deal with tied ranks in practical work: suppose that a judge ranks the 7th, 8th, 9th, 10th items equally. Then the rank that each should be given is obtained by

$\dfrac{7 + 8 + 9 + 10}{4} = \dfrac{34}{4} = 8.5$. Each item would be ranked as 8.5 and then the

formula for r (*not* r_s) used.

Setting out in a table as with r we have

	A	B	R_A	R_B	d	d^2
	8	9	2	1	1	1
	3	2	5	6	−1	1
	9	8	1	2	−1	1
	5	7	4	3	1	1
	0	4	6	4	2	4
	7	3	3	5	−2	4
TOTAL						12

The column headed d in the table is the difference $R_A - R_B$ where R_A is the ranking of judge A.

$$r_s = 1 - \frac{6 \times 12}{5 \times 24}$$

$$= 1 - \frac{72}{120}$$

$$= 1 - 0.6 = 0.4$$

The result we have obtained suggests a slight positive correlation between the two judges but that is about all that we can conclude at the moment.

There are other rank correlation coefficients, but these are not part of the 'A' level syllabus.

You should now be able to complete Exercise 4 on page 84.

Hypothesis testing and correlation

To refine our technique of interpreting the value of r or r_s we need to use the technique of hypothesis testing from Section 2. Essentially for the purposes of 'A' level this is an ability to use the tables in Appendix 4 at the end of this book.

No theoretical background is necessary concerning how the tables are obtained but simply the ability to use the tables effectively. We will illustrate their use by considering two examples.

Example   We have some bivariate data consisting of 12 pairs of numbers (i.e. $n = 12$).

We perform a calculation of r and obtain a value of 0.53.
How should we interpret this value?

Solution	We set up a null hypothesis concerning the population correlation coefficient ρ.

As in previous analyses our calculated value of r gives us an estimate for some unknown value of the population parameter (consisting of all possible pairs!). r is in fact a point estimator of ρ.

Is the value of r obtained significantly greater than zero?
We set up two hypotheses:

$$H_0 : \rho = 0$$
$$H_1 : \rho > 0 \text{ (i.e. } - \text{ a one-tailed test)}$$

and choose a significance level (5% being usual).

Referring to the tables and noting the column labelled sample size we now go to the row with 12 in it. Moving to the left we see columns marked 0.10, 0.05, etc.

We are interested in 0.05 (our 5% significance level).

The value given in the tables is 0.4973. This is the critical value. If our calculated value is greater than this value, then we will conclude that there is significant evidence that $\rho > 0$, i.e. that we should reject the null hypothesis.

In our example we found $r = 0.53$. Since $0.53 > 0.4973$ we reject H_0 in favour of H_1 at the 5% level.

Example	A calculation of r_s gives a value of 0.53 when 10 pairs of ranked items of data are compared. Is this value significant at the 5% level in a one-tailed test?

Solution	$H_0 : \rho_s = 0$	(i.e. the rank correlation for the population is hypothesised to be 0.)

$H_1 : \rho_s > 0$ (one-tailed test)

5% significance level.

Tables (the right-hand columns) give a value of 0.5636 (the critical value)

we have $r_s < 0.5636$

and so we do not reject H_0 in this case. We conclude that there is no significant rank correlation between the variables.

Two-tailed tests

It may be that the question being asked is, 'Are the variables correlated?', without the suggestion or implication of positive or negative. In such cases a two-tailed test should be conducted. The test would then take the form

$$H_0 : r = 0$$
$$H_1 : r \neq 0$$

For example if a sample of 15 pairs of items of data produced a value for r of –0.62 and we wished to test whether there was a correlation between the variables the procedure would be as follows:

$$H_0 : r = 0$$
$$H_1 : r \neq 0$$

5% significance level

two-tailed test.

As we are conducting a two-tailed test the 5% probability has to be split between the two tails giving a probability of 0.025 at each end. This is under the third column of the table and in the case of a sample size of 12 would give the reading 0.576. If our observed correlation coefficient were greater than 0.576 or less than –0.576 then we would reject H_0 and conclude significant correlation at the 5% level (but without specifying positive or negative).

A caution

It is possible to find sets of data (i.e. sets of pairs) which are highly correlated either positively or negatively, but where it would be incorrect or foolhardy to ascribe a causal connection between the two variables. It could simply be coincidence, or it may be that the two variables are correlated via a third (hidden) variable.

The numerical value of the correlation coefficient can only provide supporting mathematical evidence for a correlation which is suspected from additional evidence or observation. As an illustration it is perfectly plausible that over the last few decades life-expectancy has increased in Britain and that ownership of home computers has also increased. There is no causal connection between these variables – life expectancy has not increased as a result of more people owning home computers and nor has ownership of home computers been affected by life-expectancy. The mathematical correlation between them is related to other factors such as technological advance and increased prosperity.

You should now be able to complete Exercises 5–7 on pages 84–85.

PROJECT EXERCISES

Project work involving correlation will usually be combined with calculation of regression lines (dealt with in Section 6). There are many sources of bivariate data which may or may not exhibit correlation and the use of correlation and regression methods will be found in Geography, Economics and Science subjects.

As with all project work care should be taken in:

● defining the population of interest

● selecting an appropriate method of sampling

● providing supporting evidence for any conclusions drawn.

Here are a few more practical exercises, which cover the sorts of statistical analysis that are suitable for a project.

1 **Economics** – Is there a correlation between lowest and highest share prices for the data collected in Section 1 (Project exercise 1)?

2 **Economics** – Is there a correlation between published figures for the rate of inflation and the level of unemployment? Both sets of figures are issued monthly by the government and can be gathered from economics journals or newspapers.

3 **Sport** – Does a correlation exist between the world record time for a specific sporting event (e.g. 400 metres) and the time for which the record was in force? One might expect that as world record times improve (get shorter), the duration of each record would increase, i.e. it would stand as a record for a longer period. Is this assumption borne out by the facts?

EXERCISES

1 Find the correlation coefficient for the data in Table 5.1 for heights and weights of adult females.

2 A group of twelve children participated in a psychological study designed to assess the relationship, if any, between age, x years, and average total sleep time (ATST), y minutes. To obtain a measure for ATST, recordings were taken on each child on five consecutive nights and then averaged. The results obtained are shown below.

Child	Age (x year)	ATST (y minutes)
A	4.4	586
B	6.7	565
C	10.5	515
D	9.6	532
E	12.4	478
F	5.5	560
G	11.1	493
H	8.6	533
I	14.0	575
J	10.1	490
K	7.2	530
L	7.9	515

$\Sigma x = 108$ $\Sigma y = 6372$ $\Sigma x^2 = 1060.1$ $\Sigma y^2 = 3396942$ $\Sigma xy = 56825.4$

(a) Calculate the value of the product-moment correlation coefficient between x and y. Assess the statistical significance of your value and interpret your results.

(b) Plot these data on a scatter diagram.

Discuss, *briefly*, whether or not your conclusions in (a) should now be amended.

(c) It was subsequently discovered that Child *I* had been unwell during the study period.

Explain, *without further calculations*, the implications of this additional information on your conclusions.

[AEB]

3 A tasting panel was asked to assess biscuits baked from a new recipe. Each member of the panel was asked to assign a score on a scale from 0 to 100 for texture (X_1), flavour (X_2), sweetness (X_3), chewiness (X_4), and butteriness (X_5).

The scores assigned by the ten members of the panel for texture and flavour were as follows:

Taster	1	2	3	4	5	6	7	8	9	10
X_1	43	59	76	28	53	55	81	49	38	47
X_2	67	82	75	48	91	63	67	51	44	54

(a) Draw a scatter diagram of the data

(b) Calculate the product moment correlation coefficient between X_1 and X_2.

(c) State briefly, how you would expect the scatter diagram in (a) to alter if the tasters were given training in how to assign scores before the tasting took place.

(d) Given that $\Sigma X_3 = 601$, $\Sigma X_3^2 = 38637$ and $\Sigma X_2 X_3 = 40564$ calculate the product moment correlation coefficient between X_2 and X_3.

(e) The table below shows the product moment correlation coefficient between each pair of X_1, X_2, X_3 and X_4 (except for the two calculated in (b) and (d) which have been left blank):

	X_1	X_2	X_3	X_4
X_1	1		0.232	−0.989
X_2		1		−0.478
X_3			1	−0.251
X_4				1

If a decision was made that to save time in future only X_1, X_2 and either X_3 or X_4 would be recorded which variable (X_3 or X_4) would you omit and why?

(f) Given that the correlation coefficient between X_2 and X_5 is exactly 1, what is the correlation coefficient between X_3 and X_5?

Draw up a table showing the numerical value of the product moment correlation coefficient between each pair of X_1, X_2, X_3, X_4 and X_5.

[AEB]

4 The examination marks obtained by A, B, C, D and E are given as follows:

People	A	B	C	D	E
Mathematics mark	4.6	3.8	4.4	4	3.9
Physics mark	8	1	2	4	5

(a) Work out an order for each subject and calculate Spearman's correlation coefficient.

(b) Using the *original data*, work out the product moment correlation coefficient.

5 Six friesian cows were ranked in order of merit at an agricultural show by the official judge and by a student vet. The ranks were as follows:

Official judge	1	2	3	4	5	6
Student vet	1	5	4	2	6	3

(a) Calculate Spearman's rank correlation coefficient between these rankings.

(b) Investigate whether or not there was agreement between the rankings of the judge and the student.

State clearly your hypotheses, and carry out an appropriate one-tailed significance test at the 5% level.

6 The data below shows the height above sea level, x metres, and the temperature, $y°C$, at 7.00 a.m., on the same day in summer at 9 places in Europe.

Height (x)	1400	400	280	790	390	590	540	1250	680
Temperature (y)	6	15	18	10	16	14	13	7	13

(a) Plot these data on a scatter diagram.

(b) Calculate the product moment correlation coefficient between x and y.

(Use $\Sigma x^2 = 5639\,200$; $\Sigma y^2 = 1524$; $\Sigma xy = 66\,450$.)

(c) Give an interpretation of your coefficient.

On the same day the number of hours of sunshine was recorded and Spearman's rank correlation between hours of sunshine and temperature, based on $\Sigma d^2 = 28$ was 0.767.

(d) Stating clearly your hypotheses and using a 5% two-tailed test, interpret this rank correlation coefficient.

7 A group of students scored the following marks in their Statistics and Geography examinations.

Student	A	B	C	D	E	F	G	H
Statistics	64	71	49	38	72	55	54	68
Geography	55	50	50	47	65	45	39	82

(a) Find the value of the Spearman rank correlation coefficient between the marks of these students.

(b) Stating your hypotheses and using a 5% level of significance, interpret your value.

<table>
<tr><td>

SUMMARY

</td><td>

In this section you have investigated a variety of situations in order to discover whether there is (or is not) a relationship between two (or

</td></tr>
</table>

more) variables. The key points of the section are listed below:

● A scatter diagram gives a good impression of possible correlation

● The correlation coefficient r, measures the strength of a linear relationship:

$$-1 \leq r \leq 1$$

where $r = 1, \Rightarrow$ perfect positive correlation

$r = -1 \Rightarrow$ perfect negative correlation

● Spearman's coefficient r_s, is used to calculate the degree of correlation of ranked data

● Simple hypothesis testing for the significance of a value for r or r_s may be required.

6

Regression

In situations where calculation of the correlation coefficient or visual evidence in the form of a scatter diagram suggest a linear relationship between two variables X and Y, it may be useful to know the form that the linear relationship takes. This section deals with the problem of finding a line of best fit.

By the end of this section you should be able to:

- understand the concept of linear regression
- derive a regression equation using the method of least squares
- interpret and use a regression equation

Simple linear regression

Examples of situations where a linear model may be appropriate are:

(a) Does increasing the amount of fertiliser applied to a certain crop increase the yield?

(b) Does attendance at a training course and subsequent examination improve the performance of salespeople working for a company?

(c) Is there a linear relationship between the marks obtained in Paper I and those obtained in Paper II of an examination?

In the first two of these examples there is a degree of asymmetry in the relationship.

In example (a), for instance, we could conduct a controlled experiment in which we decide on the amount of fertiliser to apply (X) and then observe the change in yield (Y).

In example (b) we can test the relationship between the outcome of the exam (X) against the change in performance of the salespeople (Y).

In each of these cases we refer to the variable X as the **independent** or **explanatory** variable. It is something we have control over. The values of the variable Y are what we observe in response to changes in the value of X and the Y-values are consequently referred to as **dependent** or **response** variables.

In example (c) it is not so clear which variable should be called independent and which should be called dependent.

We will now look at the problem of finding a line of best fit by considering an example in some detail.

| **Example** | The accountant of a company monitors the number of items produced per month by the company, together with the total cost of production. The following table shows the data collected for a random sample of 12 months. |

Number of items (x) (1000 s)	21	39	48	24	72	75	15	35	62	81	12	56
Production cost (y) (£ 1000)	40	58	67	45	89	96	37	53	83	102	35	75

(a) Plot these data on a scatter diagram. Explain why this diagram would support the fitting of a regression equation of y on x.

(b) Find an equation for the regression line of y on x in the form $y = a + bx$.

(Use $\Sigma x^2 = 30786$; $\Sigma xy = 41\,444$)

The selling price of each item produced is £2.20.

(c) Find the level of output at which total income and total costs are equal. Interpret this value.

Solution   (a)   Figure 6.1 shows the data plotted on a scatter diagram.

Figure 6.1

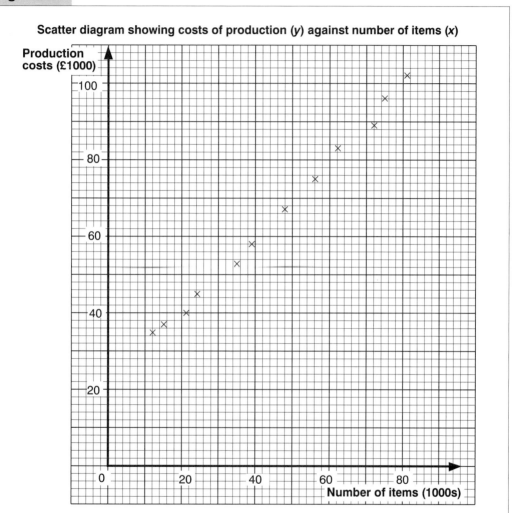

Scatter diagram showing costs of production (*y*) against number of items (*x*)

The points lie fairly closely on a straight line and so we conclude that it is worthwhile finding a regression line.

A quick calculation shows that the correlation coefficient between *x* and *y* is 0.99 which provides strong evidence for linearity when combined with the visual evidence.

(b) In this example there is a clear dependency of the variable y on the variable x. The value of x is given (it is the amount of production per month) and it is this that determines the costs for that month. So x is our explanatory variable and y is our response variable.

This part of the question asks us to find the equation of the regression line of y on x and this means finding a formula

$$y = \alpha + \beta x$$

i.e. to give y as a linear function of x.

[Later we will see that it is also possible to find a regression line of the form $x = c + dy$ which is called the regression line of x on y. In general these lines will be different.]

The problem is now reduced to using the values of the sample data to find the appropriate values of α and β. 'A' level examining boards provide the formulae necessary for calculating α and β and so it is not necessary to remember these, but certainly it is useful to have practised calculating them on many examples in order to become proficient in their use.

The formula for the regression line of y on x is

$$y = \alpha + \beta x$$

where β is estimated using the formulae

$$\hat{\beta} = \frac{S_{xy}}{S_{xx}} = \frac{\Sigma x_i y_i - n \bar{x} \bar{y}}{\Sigma x_i^2 - n \bar{x}^2}$$

and $\qquad \hat{\alpha} = \bar{y} - \hat{\beta} \bar{x}$

There is no need to worry about where these formulae come from – their derivation is difficult and not part of the 'A' level syllabus.

$\hat{\alpha}$ and $\hat{\beta}$, calculated from the sample data using the formulae above, are estimators of the population parameters α and β. A consequence of the derivation of these formulae is that **the regression lines for y on x and for x on y both pass through the point $(\bar{x}, \bar{y})$**, and that in the case of perfect correlation ($r = +1$ or $r = -1$), the lines would actually coincide.

The point $(\bar{x}, \bar{y})$ can now be indicated on the scatter diagram (as in Figure 6.2) and the regression line drawn through it.

[It is worth pointing out here that if we were calculating the regression of x on y, the same formulae would be used, except that the x's and y's would be interchanged, so that for

$$x = c + dy$$

we would have

$$\hat{d} = \frac{\Sigma x_i y_i - n\bar{x}\,\bar{y}}{\Sigma y_i^2 - n\bar{y}^2}$$

$$\hat{c} = \bar{x} - \hat{d}\bar{y}$$

i.e. there is complete symmetry in the formulae.

Which line we find, i.e. either y on x or x on y (or possibly both) depends on what it is we want to know. If we wish to predict y-values from the regression line, then it is y on x that is appropriate and for predicting x-values, then we use the regression line of x on y. If both types of prediction are required, then it is necessary to find both of the regression lines.]

As in many problems of this type, to avoid tedious calculations in examination conditions, we are provided with some summary statistics, namely

$$\Sigma x^2 = 30\ 786 \text{ and } \Sigma xy = 41\ 444$$

We also find from the table that $\bar{x} = 45$, $\bar{y} = 65$.

Using these directly in the formula for $\hat{\beta}$, we get

$$\hat{\beta} = \frac{(41\ 444) - (12)\ (45)\ (65)}{(30\ 786) - (12)\ (45)^2}$$

$$= \frac{6344}{6486} = 0.98 \text{ (2 d.p.)}$$

and $\hat{\alpha} = 65 - (0.98)\ (45)$

$$= 20.99 \text{ (2 d.p.)}$$

The line of best fit is therefore

$$y = 20.99 + 0.98\ x$$

and this now plotted on the scatter diagram (see Figure 6.2).

The simplest way to plot the line is to observe that the intercept on the y-axis is 20 and that the line must pass through $(\bar{x}, \bar{y})$.

Figure 6.2

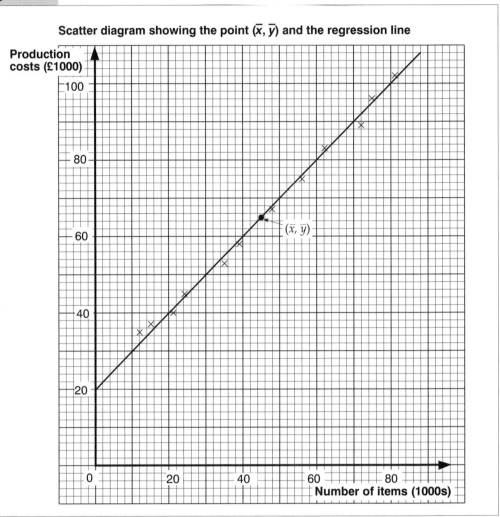

Scatter diagram showing the point $(\bar{x}, \bar{y})$ and the regression line

Alternatively, if the intercept value is not shown on the vertical axis, e.g. if it is negative or if we have used axes with 'breaks' in them, then we could just find two points on the line or use one point and $(\bar{x}, \bar{y})$.

(c)   Ignoring the fact that everything is multiplied by 1000 in the units, if x items are produced

$$\text{profit} = £2.20 \times x$$

But the total cost for producing x items is

$$y = 20.99 + 0.98x$$

If these are to be equal then we require

$$2.20x = 20.99 + 0.98x$$

$$\Rightarrow \quad 1.22x = 20.99$$

$$\Rightarrow \quad x = 17.2049$$

Therefore we would produce 17 205 items

This point represents the break-even point when costs of production are equal to total income from the production.

We will now work through another complete 'A' level question more concisely to illustrate how such a solution should be written up.

Example

Three trainee technicians carry out laboratory trials to examine the effect of temperature on the yield of an industrial process. The table shows the results obtained by each technician.

Technician	A	B	C	A	B	C	A	B	C	A	B	C
x, temperature, °C	10	15	20	25	30	35	40	45	50	55	60	65
y, yield, kg	80	106	75	90	117	118	97	127	80	109	140	115

$\Sigma x = 450 \quad \Sigma y = 1254 \quad \Sigma x^2 = 20450 \quad \Sigma xy = 49\,245$

(a) (i)   Draw a scatter diagram of the data. Label each point A, B or C according to which technician carried out the trial.

(ii)   Calculate the equation of the regression line of yield on temperature and draw the line on your scatter diagram

(iii)   Use your equation to estimate the yield for a temperature of 52°C

It is known that over this range of temperatures the relationship between yield and temperature is approximately linear.

(b)   Comment on the performance of the three trainee technicians and on the reliability of the estimate made in (a) (iii).

An experienced and reliable technician carries out the trial at a temperature of 40°C and obtains a yield of 125 kg.

(c)   Plot this point on your scatter diagram. Without further calculation modify the estimate made in (a) (iii). Comment on the reliability of your new estimate.

Solution   (a) (i)   The scatter diagram is shown in Figure 6.3.

Figure 6.3

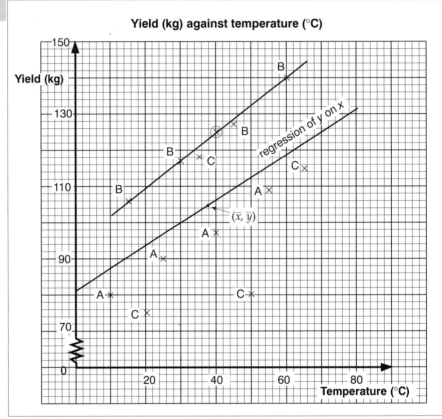

Yield (kg) against temperature (°C)

(ii)   Finding regression of y on x :

$$\bar{x} = 37.5, \quad \bar{y} = 104.5$$

$$\hat{\beta} = \frac{(49\ 245) - (12)\ (37.5)\ (104.5)}{(20\ 450) - (12)\ (37.5^2)} = 0.62\ (2\ \text{d.p.})$$

$$\hat{\alpha} = 104.5 - \hat{\beta}\ 37.5 = 81.25\ (2\ \text{d.p.})$$

giving

$$y = 81.25 + 0.62x$$

This line is now plotted on the scatter diagram (see Figure 6.3).

(iii)   If $x = 52°C$ then from the formula for the equation of the line

$$y = 113.5\ \text{kg}$$

(b) *C*'s performance is unreliable. His points do not show any linearity.

   A and *B* are both linear although they give different lines and there appears to be a constant difference between their results. We have no additional information to say which is the more accurate of *A* and *B*.

   The uncertainty described makes the prediction in (a)(iii) unreliable

(c) Point (40, 125) is plotted as ⊗ and it is now apparent that *B*'s results are more consistent with the experienced technician. A line of best fit (by eye) through the points relating to *B* and the experienced technician's point gives the upper line shown.

   Using this line our modified estimate is *y* = 134 kg when *x* = 52°C.

As a final example of calculating regression lines consider the third example referred to on page 87 where marks are given for pupils in an examination consisting of two papers.

Example   These marks out of 100 on Paper I and Paper II for a science exam are given in the following table. Draw a scatter diagram of the data and find the equations of the regression lines of *y* on *x* and *x* on *y*.

Use these equations to determine estimated marks for Candidate *J* on Paper I and for candidate *D* on Paper II who were absent for these respective papers.

	A	B	C	D	E	F	G	H	I	J	K	L	M	N	O	
Paper I	63	72	38	52	87	63	41	52	68	Abs	45	72	58	58	77	*x*
Paper II	58	59	28	Abs	85	67	48	45	64	74	53	78	51	65	61	*y*

Solution   The scatter diagram is shown in Figure 6.3.

The labelling of *x* and *y* is arbitrary

$$\bar{x} = \frac{794}{13} = 61.1$$

$$\bar{y} = \frac{762}{13} = 58.6$$

$$\Sigma x^2 = 51\ 010$$

$$\Sigma y^2 = 47\ 208$$

$$\Sigma xy = 48\ 668$$

(These values have been calculated omitting the marks for *D* and *J*.)

Figure 6.4

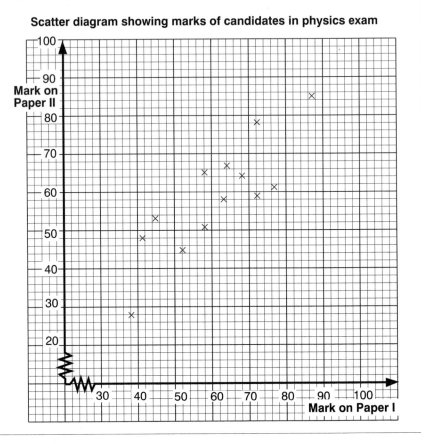

Scatter diagram showing marks of candidates in physics exam

For regression of y on x

$$\hat{\beta} = \frac{48\,665 - (13)\,(61.1)\,(58.6)}{51\,010 - (13)\,(61.1)^2} = \frac{2122.02}{2478.27} = 0.86$$

$$\hat{\alpha} = 58.6 - 0.86 \times 61.1 = 6.05$$

giving $y = 6.05 + 0.86x$

This line passes through $(\bar{x}, \bar{y})$ and $(40, 40.45)$.

For regression of x on y

$$\hat{\beta} = \frac{48\,668 - (13)\,(61.1)\,(58.6)}{47\,208 - (13)\,(58.6)^2} = \frac{2122.02}{2566.52} = 0.83$$

$$\hat{\alpha} = 61.1 - (0.79)\,(58.6) = 12.46$$

giving $x = 12.46 + 0.83y$

This line passes through $(\bar{x}, \bar{y})$ and $(80, 78.86)$.

Figure 6.5 now shows the point $(\bar{x}, \bar{y})$ and the regression lines added to the scatter diagram of Figure 6.4.

Figure 6.5

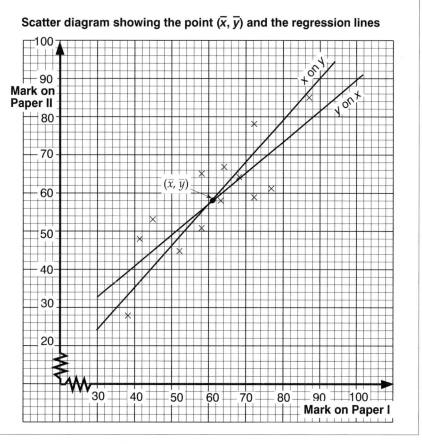

Scatter diagram showing the point $(\bar{x}, \bar{y})$ and the regression lines

We can now use either the equations or the lines on the graph to find estimates of the missing marks.

For candidate *D* we want his *y*-value when the *x*-value is 52. We use the regression of *y* on *x* for this giving

Mark on Paper II for *D* is 51.

For candidate *J*, we want his *x*-value when the *y*-value is 74. Use the regression of *x* on *y* for this to give

Mark on Paper I for *J* is 75.

Least squares

We remarked earlier that derivation of the formulae for $\hat{\alpha}$ and $\hat{\beta}$ is not part of the 'A' level syllabus. However it is worthwhile having some idea of why the method is referred to as **least squares**.

If we consider the scatter diagram below and the associated regression line (of y on x) the method of least squares effectively minimises the sum of the squares of the vertical distances of the points from the line.

Figure 6.6

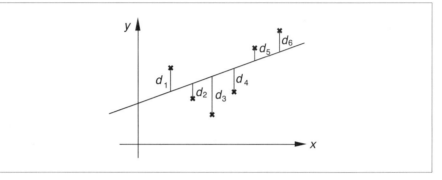

In other words the line will be chosen so that in this case the quantity

$$\sum_{i=1}^{i=6} d_i^2 \text{ will be least.}$$

The reason for choosing d_i^2 is the usual one – we need to make the distances positive, since $\sum_{i=1}^{i=6} d_i$ would be zero for a line of best fit. The problem of minimising these vertical distances involves calculus methods beyond the 'A' level syllabus. The corresponding regression line of x on y minimises the horizontal distances squared from the line.

If the line shown in Figure 6.6 is to be the line of best fit for the particular data given (y on x) and has the equation $y = mx + c$, then a way of representing the total lengths of the points from the line is given by:

$$
\begin{aligned}
R \;&=\; [y_1 - (mx_1 + c)]^2 + [y_2 - (mx_2 + c)]^2 \\
&\quad + [y_3 - (mx_3 + c)]^2 + [y_4 - (mx_4 + c)]^2 \\
&\quad + [y_5 - (mx_5 + c)]^2 + [y_6 - (mx_6 + c)]^2 \\
&=\; \sum_{i=1}^{i=6} [y_i - (mx_i + c)]^2
\end{aligned}
$$

and it is this quantity, called **the sum of the squares of the residuals**, which needs to be minimised.

Outliers

It may be that bivariate data which is collected follows an apparently linear pattern, apart from one or two exceptional cases which distort the general picture. These will sometimes occur at low or high values of x or y. It may be that these **outliers**, as they are called, are due to limitations on the linear model. In these circumstances it would be wise to reject the linear model in that region (it may still be valid elsewhere) and not use these points in calculations of $\hat{\alpha}$ and $\hat{\beta}$.

An example is shown in Figure 6.7.

Figure 6.7

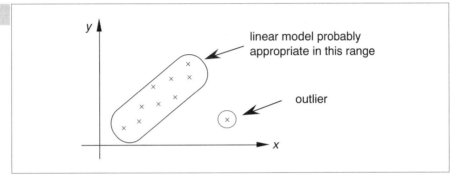

Bizarre readings within a region of suspected linearity should be treated with caution. For example:

Figure 6.8

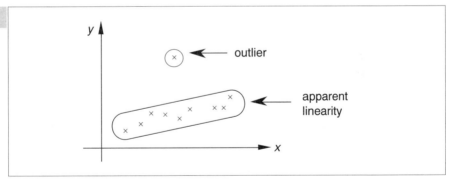

It may be that an error was made in recording that particular data item and if possible, this should be checked. It may be a genuine reading, in which case, if it is used in calculating $\hat{\alpha}$ and $\hat{\beta}$, it will distort the line of regression away from the more obviously linearly related items and thereby reduce the value of the line. Probably the wisest course of action would be to collect some more data in the region of the outlier value and confirm that it is just an isolated value. If it is not, then the linearity model will probably not be justified at all.

A caution

In some examples of linear regression there is a natural limit to the estimation process using lines of regression, e.g. in the earlier example on exam marks, there would be no call to estimate the mark on Paper II for somebody scoring 105 on Paper I since the possibility simply doesn't exist. We are confined to marks between 0 and 100 in this example.

However, in the example before, concerning the effect of temperature on yield of an industrial process, we ought to be hesitant about extrapolating much beyond the range given for the temperature in the initial data.

We would probably be safe to use B's values for predictions within the interval $0°–70°$ and possibly a little beyond, but would we want to use this line to make a prediction of yield at a temperature of, say, 250°C? Probably not – since it may be that other factors come into play at higher temperatures. We may experience 'diminishing returns', or our product may have become gaseous at that temperature. We just don't have evidence about temperatures that high and so we shouldn't make such unsafe predictions.

Similarly in the first example in this section, which was concerned with production costs, we would need to exercise caution about how the relationship continues outside the existing ranges for x and y.
The relationship between costs of production and output may cease to be linear outside the range given due to 'economies of scale'.

You should now be able to complete the Exercises on pages 101–105.

PROJECT EXERCISES

Investigations involving possible linear relationships between variables should include a clear statement of the population from which the sample is drawn and a full account of the sampling techniques employed.

A scatter diagram and calculation of a correlation coefficient are essential preliminaries to the calculation of regression lines. Note that a linear relation may be established between transformed variables, for example:

- $y = a + \dfrac{b}{x}$ represents a linear relation between $Y = y$ and $X = \dfrac{1}{x}$

- $y = ax^b$ is a linear relation between $Y = \log y$ and $X = \log x$, by rewriting as $\log y = \log a + b \log x$.

Below are a few questions involving possible linear relationships between variables. Finding answers to the questions could form the basis of a project.

1 Are 'mock' exam results a reliable way of predicting 'A' level (or GCSE) results?

2 Are absolute errors in length estimation related to absolute errors in time interval estimation? Test the validity of a linear model.

3 Is hand span linearly related to the length of the middle finger?

EXERCISES

1 Cucumbers are stored in brine before being processed into pickles. Data were collected on x, the percentage of sodium chloride in the salt used to make brine, and y, a measure of the firmness of the pickles produced. The data are shown below:

x	6.0	6.5	7.0	7.5	8.0	8.5	9.0	9.5
y	15.3	15.8	16.1	16.7	17.4	17.8	18.2	18.3

you may assume that $\Sigma x = 62$ $\Sigma x^2 = 491$ $\Sigma xy = 1060.6$ $\Sigma y = 135.6$

(a) Plot a scatter diagram of the data. Choose your scale so that values of x up to 12 will fit on the diagram.

(b) Calculate the equation of the regression line of y on x and plot the line on your diagram.

(c) Use the equation of the line to predict the value of y when x is

(i)   6.7   (ii) 10.7

Comment on these predictions.

(d) Further trials were carried out with an increased percentage of sodium chloride in the salt and the following additional observations were obtained.

x	10.0	11.0	12.0
y	18.4	18.2	18.3

Add these points to your original scatter diagram.

Modify where appropriate the predictions made in (c) and comment on your new predictions.

(*No further calculations are required for this part*)

[AEB]

2 An electric fire was switched on in a cold room and the temperature of the room was noted at five minute intervals.

Time, minutes, from switching on fire, x	0	5	10	15	20	25	30	35	40
Temperature, °C, y	0.4	1.5	3.4	5.5	7.7	9.7	11.7	13.5	15.4

You may assume that $\Sigma x = 180$ $\Sigma y = 68.8$ $\Sigma xy = 1960$ $\Sigma x^2 = 5100$

(a)   Plot the data on a scatter diagram.

(b)   Calculate the regression line $y = a + bx$ and draw it on your scatter diagram.

(c)   Predict the temperature 60 minutes from switching on the fire. Why should this prediction be treated with caution?

(d)   Starting from the equation of the regression line $y = a + bx$, derive the equation of the regression line of

   (i) y on t where y is temperature in °C (as above) and t is time in hours

   (ii) z on x where z is temperature in °K and x is time in minutes (as above)

   (A temperature in °C in converted to °K by adding 273, e.g. 10°C = 280°K.)

(e)   Explain why, in (b) the line $y = a + bx$ was calculated rather than $x = a' + b'y$.

   If, instead of the temperature being measured at 5 minute intervals, the time for the room to reach predetermined temperatures (e.g. 1, 4, 7, 10, 13°C) had been observed, what would the appropriate calculation have been? Explain your answer.

[AEB]

3 (a) State, with a reason in **each** case, but *without doing any detailed calculations*, whether or not

$$y = -1.4 + 1.6x$$

could be the least squares regression line for either of the following data sets.

(i)

x	3.7	4.4	5.6	6.2	7.3
y	4.5	5.6	7.6	8.5	10.3

(ii)

x	0.3	1.1	1.4	1.8	2.3
y	1.2	0.1	−0.4	−0.9	−1.6

(b) In an investigation of the effect of ammonia on the survival of rainbow trout reared in an intensive static-water environment, the survival rate, $y\%$, was measured at eleven fixed levels of ammonia exposure, x mg/l. The following summarised quantities were then calculated.

$\Sigma x = 220$ $\Sigma y = 860$ $\Sigma xy = 16546$ $\Sigma x^2 = 4840$ $\Sigma y^2 = 68260$

State, with a reason, an analysis you would perform on these data *prior* to a regression analysis.

Assuming that this preliminary analysis gives satisfactory results, explain why a regression line of y on x, but **not** of x on y, is appropriate.

Calculate the equation of the least squares regression line of y on x.

Hence estimate the survival rate if the level of ammonia exposure is 25 mg/l.

[AEB]

4 The following table shows the amount of water, in cm, applied to seven similar plots on an experimental farm. It also shows the yield of hay in tonnes per acre.

Amount of water (x)	30	45	60	75	90	105	120
Yield of hay (y)	4.85	5.20	5.76	6.60	7.35	7.95	7.77

(Use $\Sigma x^2 = 45675$; $\Sigma y^2 = 304.8980$; $\Sigma xy = 3648.75$)

(a) Find the equation of the regression line of y on x in the form $y = a + bx$.

(b) Interpret the coefficients of your regression line.

(c) What would you expect the yield to be for $x = 28$ and for $x = 150$? Comment on the reliability of each of your expected yields.

5 A farm food supplier monitors the number of hens kept, x, against the weekly consumption of food, y kg, for a sample of 10 small holdings.

The results are summarised below.

$\Sigma x = 360$, $\Sigma x^2 = 17362$

$\Sigma y = 286$, $\Sigma y^2 = 10928.94$, $\Sigma xy = 13773.6$

(a) Obtain the regression equation for y on x in the form $y = a + bx$.

(b) Give a practical interpretation to the slope b.

(c) If food costs £7.50 for a 25 kg bag, estimate the weekly cost of feeding 48 hens

6 An experiment was conducted into the effect of density of planting x (in plants/m^2) on the yield per plant y (in grams) of onions. Twelve observations were made as follows:

x	106.53	48.66	35.76	80.73	46.82	45.34
y	61.84	131.27	147.77	76.63	116.36	128.70

x	69.30	98.05	59.35	53.45	67.09	63.04
y	88.55	56.61	94.94	115.12	85.73	93.64

(a) Plot the points on a suitably labelled graph.

(b) Obtain the regression line of y on x in the form $y = a + bx$

(c) Give a practical interpretation to the values of a and b from such a regression line, and comment on how the value of a can be interpreted in the present case.

(d) Calculate the value of x for which the value of y in the regression line would reach O, the origin. Comment on the practical value of your result.

(e) Superimpose your regression line on the plot done in part (a). Hence discuss briefly whether a straight line appears to be an adequate model for the relationship between yield and density, and suggest an alternative, more refined model.

[$\Sigma x = 774.12$, $\Sigma x^2 = 55031.10$,
$\Sigma y = 1197.16$, $\Sigma xy = 70858.91$]

7 The sales manager of a large retailer of electrical appliances is monitoring the effects of a radio advertising campaign. Over the last seven weeks differing amounts of radio time x, in minutes, have been purchased and the corresponding numbers of sales y, in hundreds of appliances, have been recorded for the same weeks.

x (minutes)	15	8	22	11	25	18	20
y (hundreds)	16	11	20	15	26	32	20

Plot these data on a scatter diagram.

Calculate, to 2 decimal places, the value of the product moment correlation coefficient.

($\Sigma x^2 = 2243$; $\Sigma xy = 2559$; $\Sigma y^2 = 3102$)

Using your scatter diagram and the analysis carried out so far, explain why it might be inadvisable to fit a straight line regression model to these data.

In the light of your previous answer, select six points from the given data to which you could fit a straight line regression model. Explain your choice of points.

Find an equation of the regression line of y on x, giving the value of the coefficients to 2 decimal places. Give an interpretation of the slope of your line.

SUMMARY

In this section you have further investigated the relationship between variables. Through a combination of accurate diagrams and the use of calculations, you should now be able to work out the form that the linear relationship between two variables takes.

In particular you should be able to:

- calculate a regression line for y on x or x on y
- know that each of these lines passes through $(\bar{x}, \bar{y})$
- use the appropriate regression line to make predictions
- take account of limitations on the predictive ability of regression lines.

7

Tackling a Statistics project

Statistics is a highly practical subject: it has many easily identifiable applications and is an essential part of many areas of study and work. Anyone studying Economics, Politics or a science subject, such as Biology or Physics, will use statistical methods in their work time and again, e.g.:

- to analyse important economic indicators, such as changes in rates of unemployment or inflation
- to identify trends in voting patterns for different political parties across different regions
- to interpret data gained from a scientific experiment.

Because Statistics is such a practical subject, the University of London Examination and Assessment Council, like most 'A' level Examination Boards, require students to carry out a practical project as part of their 'A' level Statistics. In this section you will investigate what is involved in tackling a Statistics project. This section will also help you to make vital decisions about your project and to work through processes involved in completing a project.

By the end of this section you should be able to:

- identify a subject for a practical project
- understand and follow the procedures involved in tackling a project
- present your project clearly and attractively.

The purpose of your project

Any Statistics project you undertake will have several broad purposes:

- to show your ability to apply statistical techniques in a practical situation
- to demonstrate your mathematical skills in the use of statistical techniques
- to investigate an area or topic that is of interest to you.

The Examination Board's syllabus sets out what the overall purpose of your project should be. The current ULEAC syllabus states:

> 'The project should consist of the use of statistical methods to investigate a subject, test an assertion(s) or estimate parameters. To this end, all projects must include data collection... The purpose of the project is to demonstrate the ability to apply statistical methods in a practical situation.'

It is important that you check, at the outset, what information the Examination Board supplies in the syllabus you are working to. This information not only includes advice on important factors to bear in mind as you tackle your project, but also gives warnings about things to avoid and traps to avoid falling into.

Size of project

The syllabus gives details of the overall size of the project in terms of recommended length of time to spend on it and, importantly, the number of marks it carries towards your 'A' level.

The current (1996) ULEAC syllabus states that the project is worth 20% of the marks awarded for Module T2 and should represent about 20 hours' work.

Again, check carefully the syllabus you are working to.

A step-by-step approach

Before you begin your project, it will help to have a broad idea of the steps you will need to take:

- Plan your project. Choose a project that interests you – it is important that *you* make the choice.

- Decide what you want to find out and think how relevant it is to the work you have done. Remember your project should be *practical* and *planned* so that you can demonstrate and use the techniques covered in Modules T1 and T2. Don't collect the data first and think of things to do with it afterwards.

- Consult with your teacher/tutor for advice regarding your choice of subject, length of project, layout, strategy, etc.

- Tackle the project, consulting with your teacher/tutor as you go along.

- Collect your data – data collection is an essential part of the project. Don't just copy data from secondary sources – you won't have had any influence over the way the data has been presented and cannot be sure of its accuracy or relevance.

- Analyse the data, representing it in the most suitable form.

- Draw conclusions from your analysis.

- Ensure that your project is completed and handed in on a date agreed with your teacher/tutor, or exam centre. Remember: Examination Boards have dates fixed for receiving projects for moderation – if you miss the date because you have not completed your project, you may have to delay taking the relevant examination.

Structuring your project

Your project will be assessed through the Report that you produce at the end of it. Your report should be a carefully prepared, clearly structured and well laid out piece of work. ULEAC recommends the following components to your report – other Boards will make their own suggestions:

1   Title
2   Summary
3   Introduction
4   Data collection
5   Analysis of data
6   Interpretation
7   Conclusions

As you can see, the structure of the report reflects the different processes you have to go through in tackling the project. We will look at these in more detail.

1 Title

Choose a title which accurately describes your project, so that someone picking it up for the first time has a good idea of what subject you have investigated.

2 Summary

ULEAC recommends a summary between 100 and 200 words describing the main work undertaken and the main conclusions reached. Don't go into any detail here – aim just to give a broad picture.

3 Introduction

This should include:

- a general statement describing what subject you are investigating
- a description of your aims and objectives, including a general statement of a hypothesis or assertion you plan to test
- a description of the methods you plan to use to test the hypothesis or assertion.

Your aims should be phrased in terms of 'to investigate' or 'to test', rather than 'to show', which implies that you have already decided on the outcome of your investigations in advance.

4 Data collection

This should include:

- a description of the method used to collect data
- the reasons for choosing this method
- a description of any problems you encountered in collecting reliable data, e.g. bias, sampling
- where appropriate, a description of why the particular data (rather than other sources of information) were chosen.

There are several possible methods of data collection you could choose:

- a designed experiment
- direct observation
- questionnaires and surveys
- use of secondary data or simulation.

You may be able to use data you have collected for another subject, e.g. Biology, Economics or Chemistry.

At this stage you need to think about what precautions you could take to ensure that the data is free from bias.

- Think carefully about your sample size.
- Watch out for experimental error, e.g. does the time of day or the weather affect your results?
- Be aware of the possible drawbacks of using secondary data.
- Consider carrying out a trial or pilot study to assess the suitability of the method of data collection you have chosen.

When it comes to presenting your report, avoid putting pages and pages of data in the body of the project. Place the data in an appendix and refer to that.

5 Analysis of the data

The project should include relevant tabular and/or pictorial representations, such as grouped frequency tables, two-way tables, bar charts, pie charts, scatter graphs and line diagrams. You will have had plenty of practice at constructing these from your work on Modules T1 and T2.

The tables and diagrams you include must, however, be relevant to the aims and objectives of the project. Don't create as many different sorts of graph or diagram as you can, just because you can – you will get no credit for that. Select the most relevant representations – explaining why you chose to represent data in a particular way.

Where possible, make any comparisons on the same page.

The project should include the calculation of all relevant statistics, e.g. mean, mode, standard deviation, correlation coefficient. All appropriate workings should be shown. Again, ensure the calculations are *relevant*, not just as many as you can think of.

Where calculations are extensive, include them in an appendix, with just a summary in the body of the report.

6 Interpretation

Describe or discuss the way in which the data, diagrams and calculations have furthered the aims of your project. (You may find it clearer to include this at relevant points in your analysis of the data – see 5 above.)

7 Conclusions

The project should draw the evidence together in order to state whether or not the hypothesis or assertion made should be rejected. In some circumstances, the project may be inconclusive. This should be stated in a statement of further work which could be undertaken in order to achieve a conclusion.

Criticise your work, e.g. the sample may not have been large enough or it may have been biased because...

Be *precise* when you indicate possible areas for further study.

Examples of approaches to projects

As an example of how to approach a project, skeleton plans for a couple of possible projects are set out below.

Title: An investigation of mail deliveries

Aims:

(a)   To investigate whether the daily amount of mail my family receives follows a Poisson distribution.

(b)   To determine whether we are more likely to receive mail on any particular day of the week.

(c)   To work out what proportion of our mail is junk mail.

Data collection:

Count my family's mail for the next 100 days. Record my results in a table with the following headings.

Date	Day	Ordinary mail	Junk mail	Total mail

(These results would eventually be placed in the appendix.)

At this stage, I might also change course. For example, if the amount of mail received is very small, then it might be better to work in weeks rather than days. On the other hand, perhaps I should be distinguishing between first and second deliveries?

Analysis of data:

In terms of pictorial representation, pie charts would be appropriate.

To answer (a), calculate the sample mean and carry out a χ^2 test. Clearly state my conclusions.

To answer (b), another χ^2 test with H_0: mail equally likely on any day of the week. Clearly state my conclusions.

To answer (c), Evaluate such as $p \pm \sqrt{\dfrac{p(1-p)}{n}}$

Clearly state my conclusions.

Criticisms of my results:

The 100 days weren't random. Should I have taken a year instead? What about mislaid or mis-delivered mail? No account was taken of whether mail was first or second class. What about parcels?

Possible further studies:

Compare my results with those of one or more neighbours. Is there any correlation between the amount of junk mail received and the time of year?

| Example | A biology field trip might lead you investigate the distribution of a particular plant. |

Title: An investigation of the growth of A (whatever the plant is).

Aims:

(a)   To compare the distribution of numbers of plants on two distinct sites.

(b)   To investigate the shape of each plant – stem length v. head diameter.

(c)   To investigate the distribution of stem lengths.

Data collection:

Count the numbers of plants on two distinct sites (? the two faces of a ridge), counting the numbers of plants per square of your grid.

On one site, measure the stem lengths of the plants and their flower diameter (or some other numerical measure, depending on what kind of plant it is).

On each site, divide the area into equal sized squares, number the squares, and choose your sample squares using random numbers.

Analysis of data:

χ^2 contingency table to see if there is a significant difference between the two sites.

Correlation and regression work on stem lengths and flower diameters.

Investigate the distribution of stem lengths – is it normal? χ^2 goodness of fit.

Estimate mean and variance of population – point estimates, confidence intervals.

If other people have done similar work on the same site before (or elsewhere on the same plant), use their data as a base and perform a hypothesis test to see if there is any significant change.

At each stage, produce diagrams as well as calculations – at least they will illustrate your calculations, but they sometimes reveal features which get lost in the number crunching.

Possible further studies:

If no one else's work is available for comparison, then you could plan to repeat all or part of the project yourself, either on the same site or elsewhere.

The use of computer or calculator simulation is encouraged as a means of collecting data. Every calculator has a random number generator, but is it truly random? If it is, then the digits will be uniformly distributed over [0, 9].

Title: Random or pseudo-random numbers.

Aims:

(a)   To investigate the randomness of digits produced by a calculator.

(b)   To test the functioning of the Central Limit Theorem.

Note:

(a) is testing a null hypothesis that the numbers are U(0, 9).

(b) is testing a null hypothesis that the Central Limit theorem correctly describes the increasing normality of the sampling distribution.

Data collection and analysis:

Tally off digits from the calculator and perform a χ^2 goodness of fit of U(0, 9).

Using a programmable calculator, write a program to add the digits of, say, two random numbers (6 digits). Tally the results and perform goodness of fit against a normal distribution.

Are the mean and variance anyway what the Central Limit theorem would predict on the basis of a population of U(0, 9)?

Repeat from a larger sample size (? 18 digits).

Does the mean stay the same?

Has the variance decreased (as $\dfrac{\sigma^2}{n}$ would predict)?

Is the distribution nearer to being normal (as the Central Limit theorem claims)?

Further work: (some of this might be possible within the scope of this project, depending on how fast you work)

Repeat, using the same calculator on another occasion – does it give the same picture?

Repeat, using a different calculator.

Repeat on a computer, writing a simple programme to make the machine do most of the work for you (? use Basic, ? use a spreadsheet).

Repeat some of the work on printed random number tables (although beware of the hours of drudgery involved, with less help from machines!).

What project should you do?

The project should be of your own choosing. You will find some suggestions for project activities at the end of each section in this module. Many of them could be enlarged to the scale of a full project – if the topic is one which interests you and one in which you come up with extra ideas.

Here are a few more topic areas which you could consider as a basis for your project. The ideas are deliberately general – often little more than ideas about data you might collect. It is important that you formulate your own ideas of what to investigate, and how, and that you choose something you are interested in.

- weather in holiday resorts
- shoe size and glove/hat/dress/shirt size
- colour of cars
- journey times
- votes in a general or local election
- road accidents
- distributions of bridge hands
- poll on some location questions, e.g. use of public or private transport
- geological section
- plant population
- balance of payment, unemployment or inflation figures
- heights and weights
- effect of temperature on germination rates
- colour test of various chemical solutions
- reaction times for two groups (e.g. male, female) and other psychological experiments
- analysis of examination results
- income and expenditure among pupils
- words per page of different sorts of book
- delivery times for first and second class mail.

Tackling a survey

One of the options for data collection mentioned earlier is using a survey or questionnaire. This method has the advantage that you are actively collecting your own data. However, if you choose this approach, you must think carefully about the relevance and purpose of your survey.

Assessors see far too many projects based on surveys which have no real relevance or purpose, or are badly conducted or provide doubtful data.

If you do decide to undertake a survey, you will need to think carefully about the design of your questionnaire. Here are some tips to bear in mind:

Designing a questionnaire

- Use simple language.
- Use a small number of questions.
- Be meticulous in how you phrase questions.
- Avoid long, complicated questions.
- Be clear and unambiguous.
- Do not use leading questions.
- Avoid questions outside people's direct experience.
- Avoid embarrassing questions – the respondents may be tempted to mislead.
- Be very careful with lists of alternative answers – people's choices are sometimes based on what they remember or the first or last response in a list.
- Do not rely on people's memories.
- Consider using a pilot study to test out your questionnaire.

Getting a good mark for your project

When marking your project your assessor will be looking at all aspects of the work you have done. In particular, the following areas will be considered:

- the overall subject of the project and the problem being tackled
- the aims and objectives of the project
- the overall strategy in tackling the problem
- method of data collection chosen and effectiveness in collecting the data
- use of relevant and accurate diagrams and calculations
- interpretation of the data collected, in terms of effectiveness, accuracy, relevance, limitations, etc.
- validity of the conclusions drawn.

While it is the content of your report that you will be assessed on, it is important that you strive to make it as accessible, clear and attractive as possible.

- Your work needs to be direct and compact – don't waffle!

- Write on one side of the paper only. This way you are less likely to make mistakes and it is easier for the assessor to mark.

- Write up your work as you go along. This will save you time and will also ensure that you don't forget, or lose, anything.

- If you make a mistake, cross it out neatly and carry on.

- Consider using a typewriter or word processor to present your report.

- You can also use a computer for diagrams and calculations. If you do this, it is important to show in your report that you understand the purpose and implications of the diagrams and calculations.

SUMMARY

This section has focused on what is involved in writing an 'A' level Statistics project. It contains a great deal of advice about the structure, content and presentation of your project. Re-read the guidance given here as many times as you need to. Above all remember the following important guidelines:

- Your project needs to be practical and relevant, with a clear purpose.

- Try to choose a project that gives you the maximum opportunity to demonstrate a wide range of skills.

- Try to choose a project that you are genuinely interested in.

- Above all, discuss your project with your teacher or tutor – make the most of their advice.

Section 1

1 (a) (i) There are many solutions, such as selecting every 10th person entering a supermarket for a survey, or testing every 1000th light bulb from a production line.

(ii) Stratified sampling is generally used when the population divides naturally into sub-groups and it is desirable to sample in proportion to the numbers in the sub-groups.

(b) One major advantage of stratified sampling is that of arriving at a more representative sample where there are natural sub-groups in the population.

A disadvantage is that the sample obtained is no longer truly random.

2 Stratified

It is important to gain information from each of the departments. Stratified sampling would ensure each department is represented in the sample. The Principal might find some variation between departments, e.g. science students might be happier generally to forgo sport in favour of extra lectures. This might help decide which departments should have lectures on Wednesdays and which should not.

3 (a) $X \sim N(50, 4^2)$

$$\bar{X} \sim N\left(50, \frac{4^2}{20}\right)$$

$$P(\bar{X} > 52) = P\left(Z > \frac{52-50}{\frac{4}{\sqrt{20}}}\right)$$

$$= P(Z > 2.236) = 0.013 \text{ (3 d.p.)}$$

(b) $\bar{X} \sim N\left(38, \frac{20}{50}\right)$

$$P(\bar{X} < 36) = P\left(Z < \frac{36-38}{\sqrt{\frac{20}{50}}}\right)$$

$$= P(Z < -3.162)$$

$$= 0.001 \text{ (3 d.p.)}$$

4 Total height of boys $= 1.38 \times 15$

Total height of girls $= 1.22 \times 20$

Mean height $= \dfrac{1.38 \times 15 + 1.22 \times 20}{35}$

$$= 1.29 \text{ m}$$

5 (a) $\bar{x} = 4.6$, $s = 2$

(b) Combined mean $= 4.56$

Combined standard deviation $= 2.04$

6 (a) $\bar{x} = 6.8$, $s^2 = 5.89$

(b) $\bar{x}$ (combined) $= 7.15$

s^2 (combined) $= 6.46$

(c) Combined values are preferable as more observations are considered.

7 (a) $\mu = £4.20$ $\sigma = \sqrt{\dfrac{784}{40} - 4.2^2} = £1.40$

(b) £4.70

(c) (i) Number the amounts 00 to 39 (or equivalent) ignore others and ignore repeats.

(d) Ratio is the same as the ratio of customers i.e. $25 : 40 = 5 : 8$

Increase Dharmesh's proportion on the grounds that his data is more variable as evidenced by higher standard deviation.

Section 2

1 (a) P(25 < X < 35)

$$= P\left(\frac{25-30}{5} < Z < \frac{35-30}{5}\right)$$

$$= P(-1 < Z < 1)$$

$$= 0.683$$

(b) P($\mu - \sigma < X < \mu + \sigma$)

$$= P\left(\frac{\mu - \sigma - \mu}{\sigma} < Z < \frac{\mu + \sigma - \mu}{\sigma}\right)$$

$$= P(-1 < Z < 1)$$

$$= 0.683$$

2 90% interval $= 10.66 \pm 1.65 \cdot \dfrac{10.76}{\sqrt{2000}}$

$$= 10.66 \pm 0.397$$

$$= (10.26, 11.06)$$

3 99% interval $= 266 \pm 2.58 \times \dfrac{20}{\sqrt{40}}$

$$= 266 \pm 8.16$$

$$= (257.84, 274.16)$$

4 $\bar{x} = 1000.48$

$s^2 = 3.52$

(a) 95% interval $= 1000.48 \pm 1.96 \times \dfrac{1.88}{\sqrt{10}}$

$$= 1000.48 \pm 1.16$$

$$= (999.32, 1001.64)$$

(b) 99% interval $= 1000.48 \pm 2.5758 \times \dfrac{1.88}{\sqrt{10}}$

$$= 1000.48 \pm 1.53$$

$$= (998.95, 1002.01)$$

(c) Require $1.96 \times \dfrac{1.88}{\sqrt{n}} < 0.6$

$\Rightarrow n > 37.7$

$\Rightarrow n = 38$

5 (a) $\bar{X} \sim N\left(\mu, \dfrac{\sigma^2}{n}\right)$

(b) Require $1.96 \times \dfrac{40}{\sqrt{n}} < 15$

$\Rightarrow n > 27.3$

$\Rightarrow n$ at least 28

6 (a) P($X \leq 2$) = 0.786 (3 d.p.)

(b) P($X = 1$) = 0.326 (3 d.p.)

Confidence interval

$$= \frac{93}{2500} \pm 1.96 \sqrt{\frac{\left(\frac{93}{2500}\right)\left(\frac{2407}{2500}\right)}{2500}}$$

$$= 0.0372 \pm 0.0074$$

$$= (0.0298, 0.0446)$$

Since 0.04 is within this interval, there is probably no significant difference.

7 (a) (i) Proportion is $\dfrac{15}{40}$.

$$95\% \text{ interval is } \frac{15}{40} \pm 1.96 \sqrt{\frac{\left(\frac{15}{40}\right)\left(\frac{25}{40}\right)}{40}}$$

$$= 0.375 \pm 0.150$$

$$= (0.225, 0.525)$$

(ii) Approximate, because calculations are based on sample and calculation of confidence interval uses normal approximation to binomial.

(b) (i) $0.1 = z \sqrt{\dfrac{\left(\frac{15}{40}\right)\left(\frac{25}{40}\right)}{40}}$

$\Rightarrow z = 1.3064$

giving 90% interval

(ii) Require $1.96 \sqrt{\dfrac{\left(\frac{15}{40}\right)\left(\frac{25}{40}\right)}{n}} = 0.1$

$\Rightarrow n = 90$ would give the approximate interval asked for

Section 3

1 H_0 : observation from $X \sim N(20, 6^2)$

H_1 : observation from some other distribution

two-tailed test

5% significance

$z = \dfrac{23-20}{6} = 0.5$

$-1.96 < z < 1.96 \Rightarrow$ Accept H_0

2 $H_0 : \mu = 800$

$H_1 : \mu \neq 800$

two-tailed test

5% significance

$\bar{X} \sim N\left(800, \frac{42^2}{120}\right)$

$z = \dfrac{789-800}{\frac{42}{\sqrt{120}}} = -2.87$

Reject H_0

3 $\bar{X} \sim N\left(\mu, \dfrac{\sigma^2}{n}\right)$

(a) (9.7, 19.3)

(b) (11.8, 14.6)

(c) Evidence of decrease.

4 (a) $H_0 : \mu = 25$

$H_1 : \mu \neq 25$

two-tailed test

5% significance level

$\bar{X} \sim N\left(25, \dfrac{7.32^2}{100}\right)$

$z = \dfrac{28.7-25}{\frac{7.32}{\sqrt{100}}} = 5.05$

$\Rightarrow$ reject H_0

(b) $H_0 : \mu_1 = \mu_2$

$H_1 : \mu_1 < \mu_2$

where μ_1 = mean for Quickdry paint.

one-tailed test

5% significance level

$z = \dfrac{30.6-28.7}{\sqrt{\frac{3.51^2}{100} + \frac{7.32^2}{100}}} = 2.34 > 1.96$

$\Rightarrow$ reject H_0

(c) variation in composition

variation in atmosphere

5 (a) $H_0 : p = \frac{1}{4}$ (one in four meals is vegetarian)

$H_1 : p < \frac{1}{4}$ (less than one in four on this particular occasion)

one-tailed test

10% significance level

$z = \dfrac{\frac{2}{20} - \frac{1}{4}}{\sqrt{\frac{\left(\frac{1}{4}\right)\left(\frac{3}{4}\right)}{20}}} = -1.549$

$z < -1.282$

$\Rightarrow$ reject H_0

(b) Assumption is that the normal approximation to the binomial applies. Assumption may not hold as sample size may be too small.

6 (a) $X \sim P(10)$

$P(X \geq 12) = 0.303$

(b) $(0.303)^3 = 0.028$

(c) H_0 : mean number of typing errors/3000 words = 7.5

H_1 : mean number / 3000 words < 7.5

one-tailed test

5% significance

$z = \dfrac{4-7.5}{\sqrt{7.5}} = -1.278$

$-1.278 > -1.96$ Accept H_0.

7 $\bar{x} = 499.27$ (2 d.p.)

(a) 90% interval is $499.27 \pm 1.645 \times \dfrac{7.5}{\sqrt{11}}$

$= (495.6, 503.0)$

(b) $H_0 : \mu = 502$

$H_1 : \mu < 502$

one-tailed test

5% significance level

$z = \dfrac{499.27-502}{\frac{7.5}{\sqrt{11}}} = -1.207$

$z > -1.645 \Rightarrow$ Accept H_0.

(c) If $\mu = 496$ then z is positive and > -1.645 obviously. So no need for this one-tailed test.

8 Type I – Reject H_0 given H_0 is true

Type II – Accept H_0 given H_0 is false

(or equivalent)

(a) $\bar{x} = 7.73$ (2 d.p.) $s^2 = 36.96$ (2 d.p.)

(b) $H_0 : \mu = 10$

$H_1 : \mu < 10$

one-tailed test

5% significance level

$z = -2.89$

$z < -1.645$

$\Rightarrow$ reject H_0

Assumption is that Central Limit theorem applies.

9 P(Type I error)

$= $ P(rejecting $H_0 \,|\, H_0$ is true)

$= $ significance level of test

$= $ P(17 or more heads $\,|\, p = \frac{1}{2}$)

$= {}^{20}C_{17} \left(\frac{1}{2}\right)^{17} \left(\frac{1}{2}\right)^{3} + {}^{20}C_{18} \left(\frac{1}{2}\right)^{18} \left(\frac{1}{2}\right)^{2}$

$\quad + {}^{20}C_{19} \left(\frac{1}{2}\right)^{19} \left(\frac{1}{2}\right)^{1} + {}^{20}C_{20} \left(\frac{1}{2}\right)^{20}$

$= 1140 \left(\frac{1}{2}\right)^{20} + 190 \left(\frac{1}{2}\right)^{20} + 20 \left(\frac{1}{2}\right)^{20} + \left(\frac{1}{2}\right)^{20}$

$\Rightarrow \quad \alpha = 0.0013$

P(Type II error)

$= $ P(accepting $H_0 \,|\, H_1$ is true)

$= $ P(16 or fewer heads $\,|\, p = \frac{5}{8}$)

$= 1 - \left[\, {}^{20}C_{17} \left(\frac{5}{8}\right)^{17} \left(\frac{3}{8}\right)^{3} + {}^{20}C_{18} \left(\frac{5}{8}\right)^{18} \left(\frac{3}{8}\right)^{2} \right.$

$\qquad \left. + {}^{20}C_{19} \left(\frac{5}{8}\right)^{19} \left(\frac{3}{8}\right)^{1} + {}^{20}C_{20} \left(\frac{5}{8}\right)^{20} \, \right]$

$= 0.973$

Section 4

1 $\chi^2_{calc} = 38.2$

$\nu = 9$

$\chi^2_{5\%} = 16.92$

Reject H_0 – evidence of bias

2 $\chi^2_{calc} = 9.98$

$\nu = 4$

$\chi^2_{5\%} = 9.49$

Reject H_0 – number of calls not independent of the day of the week.

3 (a) Expected frequencies are

    12.5 50 75 50 12.5

H_0 : Data is binomial

H_1 : Data has some other distribution

5% significance

$\chi^2_{calc} = 0.5 + 6.48 + 0.48 + 2.88 + 0.5$

       $= 10.84$

$\nu = 4$

$\chi^2_{5\%} = 9.488$

Reject H_0

(b) $\bar{x} = 1.8 \Rightarrow 4p = 1.8 \Rightarrow p = 0.45$

(c) $\nu = 3$

$\chi^2_{5\%} = 7.815$

Accept H_0

(d) From tests in (a) and (c), the better model for the number of girls in a family of 4 is $X \sim B(4, 0.45)$

The chance of a girl is therefore just under $\frac{1}{2}$ at each trial.

4 (a)

x	f		$p(x)$	E	
0	8		0.0084	0.504	
1	8	} 20	0.0548	3.288	} group 13.206
2	4		0.1569	9.414	
3	10		0.2568	15.408	
4	9		0.2627	15.762	
5	7		0.1719	10.314	
6	5		0.0703	4.218	
7	3	} 14	0.0164	0.984	} group 5.304
8	6		0.0017	0.102	
	60				

(b) $p = 0.45$

H_0 : Binomial distribution B(8, 0.45) models the data

$\nu = 3$ (5 cells, 1 parameter estimated from the data and totals agree)

$\chi^2_{calc} = 23.6, \ \chi^2_{5\%} = 7.815$

Reject H_0

(c) Since binomial is not suitable model, unlikely that p is constant.

5 $\bar{x} = \dfrac{100}{37} = 2.703$

H_0 : Data comes from a Poisson distribution

H_1 : Data comes from a different distribution

x	0	1	2	3	4	5	6	7+
E	2.48	6.70	9.07	8.18	5.51	3.00	1.33	0.74

x = Number of flaws per 20 m

E = Expected frequencies (2 d.p.)

Combine cells 0 & 1

Combine cells 5, 6 and 7+

as expected frequencies less than 5.

	≤ 1	2	3	4	≥ 5
O	10	11	4	5	7
E	9.18	9.07	8.18	5.51	5.07

$\chi^2_{calc} = 3.40$

$\nu = 5 - 2 = 3$ (since $\bar{x}$ calculated from data)

$\chi^2_{5\%}(3) = 7.815, \ \chi^2_{1\%}(3) = 11.345$

Data is well within the Poisson model at both significance levels

6 $\Sigma x_i = 153\,784$
$\Sigma x_i^2 = 154\,575\,056$
(based on mid-points 993, 996,
999, 1002.5, 1006, 1009, 1012)
$\Sigma f = 153$
$\bar{x} = 1005.124$
$s^2 = 20.36$
H_0 : Data comes from a
   normal distribution
H_1 : Data comes from some
   other distribution

$a \le x < b$	$Z = \dfrac{\text{upper class boundary} - 1005.124}{4.51}$	$P(a \le X < b)$	E
$-\infty < x < 994.5$	-2.3557	0.0153	2.34
$994.5 \le x < 997.5$	-1.6905	0.0361	5.52
$997.5 \le x < 1000.5$	-1.0253	0.1072	16.40
$1000.5 \le x < 1004.5$	-0.1384	0.2883	44.12
$1004.5 \le x < 1007.5$	-0.5268	0.2599	39.76
$1007.5 \le x < 1010.5$	1.1920	0.1710	26.16
$1010.5 \le x < \infty$	∞	0.1222	18.67
		1.0000	153

We have to pool the first two classes as 2.34 < 5.
χ^2 is therefore calculated from the table.

O	E
10	7.86
15	16.40
32	44.12
51	39.76
27	26.16
18	18.67

$\chi^2_{calc} = 7.26$
$v = 6 - 2 - 1 = 3$
$\chi^2_{5\%}(3) = 7.815$
Accept H_0.
Normal distribution is a good fit at the 5% level.

7 $\Sigma x_i = 801$
$\Sigma x_i^2 = 14\,470.25$
$\Sigma f = 54$
$\Rightarrow \bar{x} = 14.833$
$s^2 = 48.844$
H_0 : Data has normal
   distribution
H_1 : Data has some other
   distribution

$a < x \le b$	$Z = \dfrac{b - 14.833}{6.989}$	$P(a < X \le b)$	E
$-\infty < x < 5.5$	-1.34	0.090	4.865
$5.5 \le x < 10.5$	-0.62	0.179	9.671
$10.5 \le x < 15.5$	0.10	0.272	14.699
$15.5 \le x < 20.5$	0.81	0.251	13.565
$20.5 \le x < 25.5$	1.53	0.146	7.884
$25.5 \le x < \infty$	∞	0.062	3.316
		1.000	54

The first two and the last two classes must be pooled. This gives the following table.

O	E
16	14.537
14	14.699
13	13.565
11	11.200

$\chi^2_{calc} = 0.603$

$v = 4 - 2 - 1 = 1$

$\chi^2_{5\%} (1) = 3.841$

Accept the hypothesis that the normal distribution is a good fit at the 5% level.

8 H_0 : no association $\Big\}$ between type
H_1 : association $\Big\}$ and cover

Expected frequencies

	N	T	G
H	33.6	7.47	14.93
P	56.4	12.53	25.07

$v = (3 - 1)(2 - 1) = 2$

$\chi^2_{calc} = 11.09$

$\chi^2_{5\%} (2) = 5.99$

Reject H_0

There is an association.

9 H_0 (independence)

Expected frequencies are

	C	P	F
A	48	10.7	21.3
B	42	9.3	18.7

$v = 2$

$\chi^2_{calc} = 0.1875 + 0.0458 + 0.2484 + 0.2143$
$+ 0.0527 + 0.2829 = 1.032$

$\chi^2_{5\%} (2) = 5.99$

Accept H_0

10 (a) Expected frequencies as follows

	F	R
μ	36.7	18.3
F	23.3	11.7

$\chi^2_{calc} = \dfrac{(\,|\,39 - 36.7\,|\, - \frac{1}{2})^2}{36.7}$

$+ \dfrac{(\,|\,16 - 18.3\,|\, - \frac{1}{2})^2}{18.3}$

$+ \dfrac{(\,|\,21 - 23.3\,|\, - \frac{1}{2})^2}{23.3}$

$+ \dfrac{(\,|\,14 - 11.7\,|\, - \frac{1}{2})^2}{11.7}$

$= 0.0883 + 0.1770 + 0.1391 + 0.2769$

$= 0.6813$

$\chi^2_{5\%} (1) = 3.841$

Accept H_0.

(b) Observed:

	F/R	P	S	
M	17	8	10	35
F	31	17	37	85
	48	25	47	120

Expected:

14	7.3	13.7
34	17.7	33.3

$\chi^2_{calc} = 0.643 + 0.067 + 0.999 + 0.265$
$+ 0.028 + 0.411$

$= 2.413$

$\chi^2_{5\%} (2) = 5.991$

Accept H_0 (independence)

French/Russian combined as observed French < 5 and these are known to be independent.

(c) French decreased in popularity. Female Russian students increased in spite of alternatives.

Section 5

1 $r = \dfrac{1123.54}{\sqrt{393.06 \times 3710.65}} = 0.93$

2   (a) $r = -0.481$

$H_0 : \rho = 0$

$H_1 : \rho < 0$ 5% significance

Critical value = -0.4973

Accept H_0

See scatter diagram below.

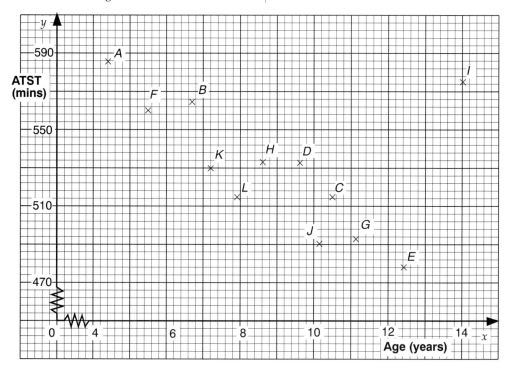

No correlation.

(b)   Conclusion should be amended.

There is a trend with I as serious outlier.

(c)   Child I needed more sleep owing to illness

3   (b) $r_2 = 0.549$

(c)   become closer to straight line

(d) $r_3 = 0.858$

(e)   Omit X_4 – 'chewiness' is highly negatively correlated with the others.

(f)   0.858

	X_1	X_2	X_3	X_4	X_5
X_1	1	0.549	0.232	–0.989	0.549
X_2		1	0.858	–0.478	1
X_3			1	–0.251	0.858
X_4				1	–0.478
X_5					1

4 (a) The subject orders are as follows:

	A	B	C	D	E
Maths	1	5	2	3	4
Physics	1	5	4	3	2

$\therefore d \qquad 0 \quad 0 \quad -2 \quad 0 \quad 2$

$\therefore \Sigma d^2 = 0 + 0 + (-2)^2 + 0 + 2^2 = 8$

$\therefore r_s = 1 - \dfrac{6 \times 8}{5(5^2 - 1)} = 0.6$

(b) $\bar{M} = 4.14,$

$\text{Var}(M) = 0.0944$

$\bar{P} = 4$

$\text{Var}(P) = 6, \ \Sigma MP = 84.9, \ \text{Covariance} = 0.42$

$\therefore r = \dfrac{0.42}{\sqrt{0.0944 \times 6}} = 0.56$

5 (a) 0.314

(b) $H_0 : \rho_s = 0$

$H_1 : \rho_s > 0$

Accept H_0 – no agreement

6 (a) The scatter diagram is shown below.

(b) -0.98

(c) Strong negative correlation suggests as height increases temperature decreases

(d) $H_0 : \rho_s = 0$

$H_1 : \rho_s > 0$

Reject H_0 – association exists.

7 (a) 0.637

(b) $H_0 : \rho_s = 0$

$H_1 : \rho_s > 0$

Accept H_0

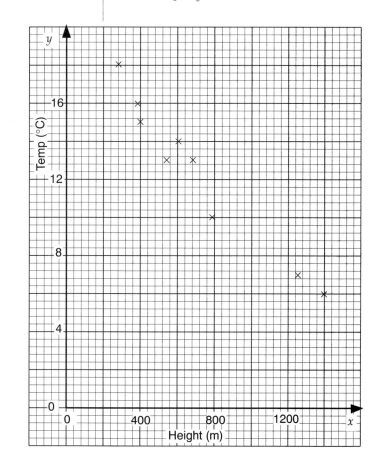

Section 6

1 (a) See graph

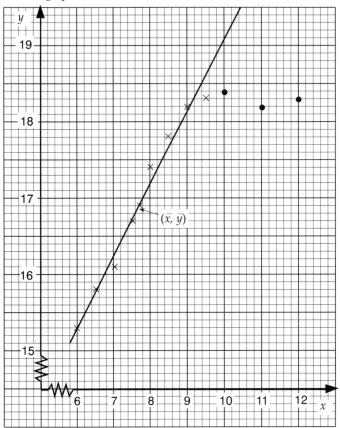

(b) $y = 9.789 + 0.924\,x$

(c) (i) $y = 15.98$ (ii) $y = 19.68$

The first is probably reliable, but not the second as it lies outside the interval for x-values.

(d) Modify (c)(ii) to approx $y = 18.3$.

Appears to be levelling off to constant value.

2 (a) See graph below.

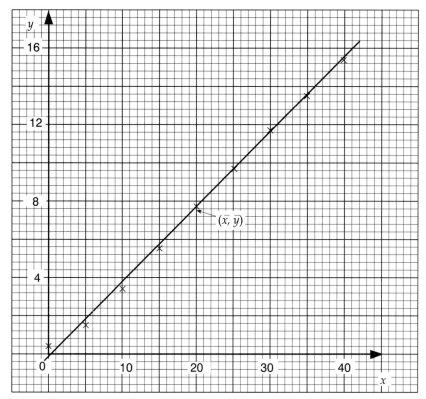

(b) $y = -0.14 + 0.39x$

(c) $x = 60$, $y = 23.24$ Unsafe prediction since outside range of x-values

(d) (i) $y = -0.16 + 23.2t$

(ii) $z = -0.16 + 0.39x + 273$

(e) x is the independent or explanatory variable. Regression of x on y.

3 (a) (i) Yes

(ii) No (by substituting some values)

(b) Calculation of correlation coefficient, draw scatter diagram, x is the explanatory variable

$y = 107.91 - 1.49x$ 70.7%

4 (a) $y = 3.67 + 0.038x$

(b) If no water applied 3.67 tonnes/acre will be the yield

For every extra cm of water an additional 0.038 tonnes will be gained

(c) $x = 28$ gives $y = 4.72$ reliable since within the range of x-values given $(30 - 120)$

$x = 150$ gives $y = 9.33$ probably unreliable since outside this interval.

5 (a) $y = 0.16 + 0.79x$

(b) A hen consumes 0.79 kg of food each week

(c) £11.43

6 (b) $y = 180.5 - 1.25x$

(c) b = yield per density, a = yield when density is zero. No sensible interpretation of a therefore.

(d) 144.32. The value of the density when yield becomes zero

(e) See graph. Not adequate model, yx = constant is more plausible.

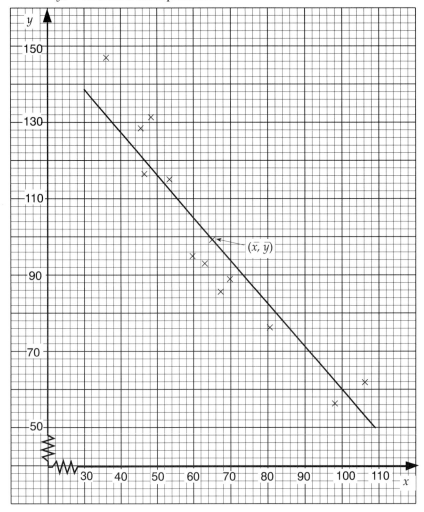

7 $r = 0.694$

One point (18, 32) is an outlier.
Use all points except this one.
$b = 0.75$
$a = 5.31$
gives $y = 5.31 + 0.75x$

The interpretation of $b = 0.75$ is that every minute of advertising produced $0.75 \times 100 = 75$ sales.

Appendix 1: Random numbers

86 13	84 10	07 30	39 05	97 96	88 07	37 26	04 89	13 48	19 20
60 78	48 12	99 47	09 46	91 33	17 21	03 94	79 00	08 50	40 16
78 48	03 37	82 26	01 06	64 65	94 41	17 26	74 66	61 93	24 97
80 56	90 79	66 94	18 40	97 79	93 20	41 51	25 04	20 71	76 04
99 09	39 25	66 31	70 56	30 15	52 17	87 55	31 11	10 68	98 23
56 32	32 72	91 65	97 36	56 61	12 79	95 17	57 16	53 58	96 36
66 02	49 93	97 44	99 15	56 86	80 57	11 78	40 23	58 40	86 14
31 77	53 94	05 93	56 14	71 23	60 46	05 33	23 72	93 10	81 23
98 79	72 43	14 76	54 77	66 29	84 09	88 56	75 86	41 67	04 42
50 97	92 15	10 01	57 01	87 33	73 17	70 18	40 21	24 20	66 62
90 51	94 50	12 48	88 95	09 34	09 30	22 27	25 56	40 76	01 59
31 99	52 24	13 43	27 88	11 39	41 65	00 84	13 06	31 79	74 97
22 96	23 34	46 12	67 11	48 06	99 24	14 83	78 37	65 73	39 47
06 84	55 41	27 06	74 59	14 29	20 14	45 75	31 16	05 41	22 96
08 64	89 30	25 25	71 35	33 31	04 56	12 67	03 74	07 16	49 32
86 87	62 43	15 11	76 49	79 13	78 80	93 89	09 57	07 14	40 74
94 44	97 13	77 04	35 02	12 76	60 91	93 40	81 06	85 85	72 84
63 25	55 14	66 47	99 90	02 90	83 43	16 01	19 69	11 78	87 16
11 22	83 98	15 21	18 57	53 42	91 91	26 52	89 13	86 00	47 61
01 70	10 83	94 71	13 67	11 12	36 54	53 32	90 43	79 01	95 15

Appendix 2: The normal distribution function

The function tabulated below is $\Phi(z)$, defined as $\Phi(z) = \dfrac{1}{\sqrt{2\pi}} \displaystyle\int_{-\infty}^{z} e^{-\frac{1}{2}t^2}\, dt.$

z	$\Phi(z)$	z	$\Phi(z)$	z	$\Phi(z)$	z	$\Phi(z)$	z	$\Phi(z)$
0.00	0.5000	0.50	0.6915	1.00	0.8413	1.50	0.9332	2.00	0.9772
0.01	0.5040	0.51	0.6950	1.01	0.8438	1.51	0.9345	2.02	0.9783
0.02	0.5080	0.52	0.6985	1.02	0.8461	1.52	0.9357	2.04	0.9793
0.03	0.5120	0.53	0.7019	1.03	0.8485	1.53	0.9370	2.06	0.9803
0.04	0.5160	0.54	0.7054	1.04	0.8508	1.54	0.9382	2.08	0.9812
0.05	0.5199	0.55	0.7088	1.05	0.8531	1.55	0.9394	2.10	0.9821
0.06	0.5239	0.56	0.7123	1.06	0.8554	1.56	0.9406	2.12	0.9830
0.07	0.5279	0.57	0.7157	1.07	0.8577	1.57	0.9418	2.14	0.9838
0.08	0.5319	0.58	0.7190	1.08	0.8599	1.58	0.9429	2.16	0.9846
0.09	0.5359	0.59	0.7224	1.09	0.8621	1.59	0.9441	2.18	0.9854
0.10	0.5398	0.60	0.7257	1.10	0.8643	1.60	0.9452	2.20	0.9861
0.11	0.5438	0.61	0.7291	1.11	0.8665	1.61	0.9463	2.22	0.9868
0.12	0.5478	0.62	0.7324	1.12	0.8686	1.62	0.9474	2.24	0.9875
0.13	0.5517	0.63	0.7357	1.13	0.8708	1.63	0.9484	2.26	0.9881
0.14	0.5557	0.64	0.7389	1.14	0.8729	1.64	0.9495	2.28	0.9887
0.15	0.5596	0.65	0.7422	1.15	0.8749	1.65	0.9505	2.30	0.9893
0.16	0.5636	0.66	0.7454	1.16	0.8770	1.66	0.9515	2.32	0.9898
0.17	0.5675	0.67	0.7486	1.17	0.8790	1.67	0.9525	2.34	0.9904
0.18	0.5714	0.68	0.7517	1.18	0.8810	1.68	0.9535	2.36	0.9909
0.19	0.5753	0.69	0.7549	1.19	0.8830	1.69	0.9545	2.38	0.9913
0.20	0.5793	0.70	0.7580	1.20	0.8849	1.70	0.9554	2.40	0.9918
0.21	0.5832	0.71	0.7611	1.21	0.8869	1.71	0.9564	2.42	0.9922
0.22	0.5871	0.72	0.7642	1.22	0.8888	1.72	0.9573	2.44	0.9927
0.23	0.5910	0.73	0.7673	1.23	0.8907	1.73	0.9582	2.46	0.9931
0.24	0.5948	0.74	0.7704	1.24	0.8925	1.74	0.9591	2.48	0.9934
0.25	0.5987	0.75	0.7734	1.25	0.8944	1.75	0.9599	2.50	0.9938
0.26	0.6026	0.76	0.7764	1.26	0.8962	1.76	0.9608	2.55	0.9946
0.27	0.6064	0.77	0.7794	1.27	0.8980	1.77	0.9616	2.60	0.9953
0.28	0.6103	0.78	0.7823	1.28	0.8997	1.78	0.9625	2.65	0.9960
0.29	0.6141	0.79	0.7852	1.29	0.9015	1.79	0.9633	2.70	0.9965
0.30	0.6179	0.80	0.7881	1.30	0.9032	1.80	0.9641	2.75	0.9970
0.31	0.6217	0.81	0.7910	1.31	0.9049	1.81	0.9649	2.80	0.9974
0.32	0.6255	0.82	0.7939	1.32	0.9066	1.82	0.9656	2.85	0.9978
0.33	0.6293	0.83	0.7967	1.33	0.9082	1.83	0.9664	2.90	0.9981
0.34	0.6331	0.84	0.7995	1.34	0.9099	1.84	0.9671	2.95	0.9984
0.35	0.6368	0.85	0.8023	1.35	0.9115	1.85	0.9678	3.00	0.9987
0.36	0.6406	0.86	0.8051	1.36	0.9131	1.86	0.9686	3.05	0.9989
0.37	0.6443	0.87	0.8078	1.37	0.9147	1.87	0.9693	3.10	0.9990
0.38	0.6480	0.88	0.8106	1.38	0.9162	1.88	0.9699	3.15	0.9992
0.39	0.6517	0.89	0.8133	1.39	0.9177	1.89	0.9706	3.20	0.9993
0.40	0.6554	0.90	0.8159	1.40	0.9192	1.90	0.9713	3.25	0.9994
0.41	0.6591	0.91	0.8186	1.41	0.9207	1.91	0.9719	3.30	0.9995
0.42	0.6628	0.92	0.8212	1.42	0.9222	1.92	0.9726	3.35	0.9996
0.43	0.6664	0.93	0.8238	1.43	0.9236	1.93	0.9732	3.40	0.9997
0.44	0.6700	0.94	0.8264	1.44	0.9251	1.94	0.9738	3.50	0.9998
0.45	0.6736	0.95	0.8289	1.45	0.9265	1.95	0.9744	3.60	0.9998
0.46	0.6772	0.96	0.8315	1.46	0.9279	1.96	0.9750	3.70	0.9999
0.47	0.6808	0.97	0.8340	1.47	0.9292	1.97	0.9756	3.80	0.9999
0.48	0.6844	0.98	0.8365	1.48	0.9306	1.98	0.9761	3.90	1.0000
0.49	0.6879	0.99	0.8389	1.49	0.9319	1.99	0.9767	4.00	1.0000
0.50	0.6915	1.00	0.8413	1.50	0.9332	2.00	0.9772		

Percentage points of the normal distribution

The values z in the table are those which a random variable $Z \sim N(0, 1)$ exceeds with probability p; that is, $P(Z > z) = 1 - \Phi(z) = p$.

p	z	p	z
0.5000	0.0000	0.05000	1.6449
0.4000	0.2533	0.0250	1.9600
0.3000	0.5244	0.0100	3.3263
0.2000	0.8416	0.0050	2.5758
0.1500	1.0364	0.0010	3.0902
0.1000	1.2816	0.0005	3.2905

Appendix 3: Percentage points of the χ^2 distribution

The values in the table are those which a random variable with the χ^2 distribution on v degrees of freedom exceeds with the probability shown.

v	0.995	0.990	0.975	0.950	0.900	0.100	0.050	0.025	0.010	0.005
1	0.000	0.000	0.001	0.004	0.016	2.705	3.841	5.024	6.635	7.879
2	0.010	0.020	0.051	0.103	0.211	4.605	5.991	7.378	9.210	10.597
3	0.072	0.115	0.216	0.352	0.584	6.251	7.815	9.348	11.345	12.838
4	0.207	0.297	0.484	0.711	1.064	7.779	9.488	11.143	13.277	14.860
5	0.412	0.554	0.831	1.145	1.610	9.236	11.070	12.832	15.086	16.750
6	0.676	0.872	1.237	1.635	2.204	10.645	12.592	14.449	16.812	18.548
7	0.989	1.239	1.690	2.167	2.833	12.017	14.067	16.013	18.475	20.278
8	1.344	1.646	2.180	2.733	3.490	13.362	15.507	17.535	20.090	21.955
9	1.735	2.088	2.700	3.325	4.168	14.684	16.919	19.023	21.666	23.589
10	2.156	2.558	3.247	3.940	4.865	15.987	18.307	20.483	23.209	25.188
11	2.603	3.053	3.816	4.575	5.580	17.275	19.675	21.920	24.725	26.757
12	3.074	3.571	4.404	5.226	6.304	18.549	21.026	23.337	26.217	28.300
13	3.565	4.107	5.009	5.892	7.042	19.812	22.362	24.736	27.688	29.819
14	4.075	4.660	5.629	6.571	7.790	21.064	23.685	26.119	29.141	31.319
15	4.601	5.229	6.262	7.261	8.547	22.307	24.996	27.488	30.578	32.801
16	5.142	5.812	6.908	7.962	9.312	23.542	26.296	28.845	32.000	34.267
17	5.697	6.408	7.564	8.672	10.085	24.769	27.587	30.191	33.409	35.718
18	6.265	7.015	8.231	9.390	10.865	25.989	28.869	31.526	34.805	37.156
19	6.844	7.633	8.907	10.117	11.651	27.204	30.144	32.852	36.191	38.582
20	7.434	8.260	9.591	10.851	12.443	28.412	31.410	34.170	37.566	39.997
21	8.034	8.897	10.283	11.591	13.240	29.615	32.671	35.479	38.932	41.401
22	8.643	9.542	10.982	12.338	14.042	30.813	33.924	36.781	40.289	42.796
23	9.260	10.196	11.689	13.091	14.848	32.007	35.172	38.076	41.638	44.181
24	9.886	10.856	12.401	13.848	15.659	33.196	36.415	39.364	42.980	45.558
25	10.520	11.524	13.120	14.611	16.473	34.382	37.652	40.646	44.314	46.928
26	11.160	12.198	13.844	15.379	17.292	35.563	38.885	41.923	45.642	48.290
27	11.808	12.879	14.573	16.151	18.114	36.741	40.113	43.194	46.963	49.645
28	12.461	13.565	15.308	16.928	18.939	37.916	41.337	44.461	48.278	50.993
29	13.121	14.256	16.047	17.708	19.768	39.088	42.557	45.722	49.588	52.336
30	13.787	14.953	16.791	18.493	20.599	40.256	43.773	46.979	50.892	53.672

Appendix 4: Critical values for correlation coefficients

These tables concern tests of the hypothesis that a population correlation coefficient ρ is 0. The values in the tables are the minimum values which need to be reached by a sample correlation coefficient in order to be significant at the level shown, on a one-tailed test.

Product Moment Coefficient					Sample size	Spearman's Coefficient		
Level						Level		
0.10	0.05	0.025	0.01	0.005		0.05	0.025	0.01
0.8000	0.9000	0.9500	0.9800	0.9900	4	1.0000	–	–
0.6870	0.8054	0.8783	0.9343	0.9587	5	0.9000	1.0000	1.0000
0.6084	0.7293	0.8114	0.8822	0.9172	6	0.8286	0.8857	0.9429
0.5509	0.6694	0.7545	0.8329	0.8745	7	0.7143	0.7857	0.8929
0.5067	0.6215	0.7067	0.7887	0.8343	8	0.6429	0.7381	0.8333
0.4716	0.5822	0.6664	0.7498	0.7977	9	0.6000	0.7000	0.7833
0.4428	0.5494	0.6319	0.7155	0.7646	10	0.5636	0.6485	0.7455
0.4187	0.5214	0.6021	0.6851	0.7348	11	0.5364	0.6182	0.7091
0.3981	0.4973	0.5760	0.6581	0.7079	12	0.5035	0.5874	0.6783
0.3802	0.4762	0.5529	0.6339	0.6835	13	0.4835	0.5604	0.6484
0.3646	0.4575	0.5324	0.6120	0.6614	14	0.4637	0.5385	0.6264
0.3507	0.4409	0.5140	0.5923	0.6411	15	0.4464	0.5214	0.6036
0.3383	0.4259	0.4973	0.5742	0.6226	16	0.4294	0.5029	0.5824
0.3271	0.4124	0.4821	0.5577	0.6055	17	0.4142	0.4877	0.5662
0.3170	0.4000	0.4683	0.5425	0.5897	18	0.4014	0.4716	0.5501
0.3077	0.3887	0.4555	0.5285	0.5751	19	0.3912	0.4596	0.5351
0.2992	0.3783	0.4438	0.5155	0.5614	20	0.3805	0.4466	0.5218
0.2914	0.3687	0.4329	0.5034	0.5487	21	0.3701	0.4364	0.5091
0.2841	0.3598	0.4227	0.4921	0.5368	22	0.3608	0.4252	0.4975
0.2774	0.3515	0.4133	0.4815	0.5256	23	0.3528	0.4160	0.4862
0.2711	0.3438	0.4044	0.4716	0.5151	24	0.3443	0.4070	0.4757
0.2653	0.3365	0.3961	0.4622	0.5052	25	0.3369	0.3977	0.4662
0.2598	0.3297	0.3882	0.4534	0.4958	26	0.3306	0.3901	0.4571
0.2546	0.3233	0.3809	0.4451	0.4869	27	0.3242	0.3828	0.4487
0.2497	0.3172	0.3739	0.4372	0.4785	28	0.3180	0.3755	0.4401
0.2451	0.3115	0.3673	0.4297	0.4705	29	0.3118	0.3685	0.4325
0.2407	0.3061	0.3610	0.4226	0.4629	30	0.3063	0.3624	0.4251
0.2070	0.2638	0.3120	0.3665	0.4026	40	0.2640	0.3128	0.3681
0.1843	0.2353	0.2787	0.3281	0.3610	50	0.2353	0.2791	0.3293
0.1678	0.2144	0.2542	0.2997	0.3301	60	0.2144	0.2545	0.3005
0.1550	0.1982	0.2352	0.2776	0.3060	70	0.1982	0.2354	0.2782
0.1448	0.1852	0.2199	0.2597	0.2864	80	0.1852	0.2201	0.2602
0.1364	0.1745	0.2072	0.2449	0.2702	90	0.1745	0.2074	0.2453
0.1292	0.1654	0.1966	0.2324	0.2565	100	0.1654	0.1967	0.2327